STRIVING

HUNTER COLLEGE
GATEWAY ENGLISH CURRICULUM DEVELOPMENT STAFF

Selection of the works included in these anthologies and the development of their accompanying teaching approaches and aids have been in a genuine sense a cooperative endeavor involving experienced classroom and college teachers. Although smaller groups of the total staff had special responsibility for individual units, each unit was discussed by the full staff at various stages.

Curriculum Development Staff:

Mr. Frank E. Brown, Teacher of English, New York City Public Schools

Mr. Richard Corbin, Chairman of English, Hunter College High School; President of N.C.T.E., 1964–1965

Mr. Richard B. Davis, Audio-Visual Specialist

Dr. Florence B. Freedman, Associate Professor of Education, Hunter College

Mrs. Evelyn Gott, Teacher of English, Long Lots Junior High School, Westport, Connecticut

Miss Mary Delores Jarmon, Teacher of English, Cleveland Public Schools

Miss Edna V. Kane, Administrative Assistant to the Director

Mr. John J. Marcatante, Chairman of English, Astoria Junior High School, New York City

Mr. John G. McMeekin, Formerly elementary teacher, Mentor Public Schools, Ohio

Miss Lynne McVeigh, Audio-Visual Specialist

Mrs. Sally-Anne Milgrim, Department of Education, Hunter College

Mrs. Sandra E. Motz, Formerly teacher of English and Drama, Agricultural and Technical College, Greensboro, North Carolina

Mrs. Domenica Paterno, Teacher of English, Hunter College High School

Dr. Marjorie B. Smiley, Professor of Education, Hunter College; Director of Hunter College Project English Curriculum Center

Mr. Charles G. Spiegler, Chairman of English, Central Commercial High School, New York City

Miss Jacqueline Tilles, Teacher of English, Detroit Public Schools

Others who have assisted:

Miss Betty Broder, Hunter College student

Mrs. Merry H. Renert, Hunter College student

Miss Mary Shaub, Hunter College student

Mr. Sanford Rosenblum, Sanford Graphics

Mr. Marc Strausberg, Selected Academic Readings

MACMILLAN GATEWAY ENGLISH

A Literature and Language Arts Program

STRIVING

Marjorie B. Smiley • Charles G. Spiegler

John J. Marcatante • Jacqueline Tilles

The Macmillan Company, New York

The research reported herein was supported through the Cooperative Research Program of the Office of Education, U. S. Department of Health, Education, and Welfare, and Hunter College of the City University of New York.

ACKNOWLEDGMENTS

We especially wish to thank the students whose interest and enthusiasm in the preliminary use of the Hunter College *Gateway English* anthologies encouraged us in our efforts to meet their expectations. To these students also we owe a number of suggestions which have been incorporated into the books and recommended classroom activities.

For permission to use material in this book, grateful acknowledgment is made to the following:

Abingdon Press: For "Scarface" by George Bird Grinnell. From *Hero Tales from Many Lands* selected by Alice I. Hazeltine.

CBS Television Network: For "Express Stop from Lenox Avenue," by Adrian Spies. From *The Doctors and the Nurses*, Plautus Productions, Inc. Used by special permission of CBS Television Network and Plautus Productions, Inc. © Plautus Productions, Inc. 1963. All Rights Reserved.

The Macmillan Company, New York
Collier-Macmillan Canada, Ltd., Toronto, Ontario
Printed in the United States of America

Curtis Brown Ltd.: For "Manhood" by John Wain. From *Death of the Hind Legs*.

Farrar, Straus & Giroux, Inc.: For "Daedalus and Icarus." Reprinted with permission of Farrar, Straus & Giroux, Inc. and MacGibbon & Kee, Ltd., from *Men and Gods* by Rex Warner. All rights reserved.

Holt, Rinehart and Winston, Inc.: For Chapters 4 and 5. From *Nellie Bly* by Nina Brown Baker. Copyright © 1965 by Nina Brown Baker. Reprinted by permission of Holt, Rinehart and Winston, Inc.

Dr. Frank Horne: For "To James." From *Golden Slippers* compiled by Arna Bontemps. Reprinted by permission of the author.

Alfred A. Knopf, Inc.: For "Mother to Son." From *Selected Poems*, by Langston Hughes. Copyright 1926 by Alfred A. Knopf, Inc. and renewed 1954 by Langston Hughes. Reprinted by permission of Alfred A. Knopf, Inc.

MacGibbon & Kee, Ltd.: For "Through the Tunnel" from *The Habit of Loving* by Doris Lessing. For "Daedalus and Icarus" from *Men and Gods* by Rex Warner. Both reprinted by permission of MacGibbon & Kee, Ltd.

McGraw-Hill Book Co.: For "No Hero." From *A Jesse Stuart Reader* by Jesse Stuart. Copyright © 1963 by McGraw-Hill Inc. Used by permission of McGraw-Hill Book Company.

The News: For "It's Her Way" by Walter C. Meyer. Courtesy of *The News, New York's Picture Newspaper*.

Phelps-Stokes Fund: For "The Parable of the Eagle" by James Aggrey from *Aggrey of Africa* by Edwin Smith. Used by permission of Phelps-Stokes Fund.

Paul R. Reynolds Inc.: For "Antaeus" by Borden Deal. From *Southwest Review*. Copyright © 1961 by Southern Methodist University Press Inc. Reprinted by permission of Paul R. Reynolds Inc., 599 Fifth Avenue, New York 17, N.Y.

Scholastic Magazines, Inc.: For "Skepticism" by Ruby-Luse from *Scholastic Scope*. Reprinted by permission from *Scholastic Scope*, © 1966 by Scholastic Magazines, Inc.

A. D. Schulberg: For "The Wonderful Lousy Poem" by Budd Schulberg. © 1964 by *Family Weekly*. Reprinted by permission.

Southern Methodist University Press: For "Antaeus" by Borden Deal from *Southwest Review*, Spring 1961. © 1961 by Southern Methodist University Press. Reprinted by permission of the publisher and the author.

Photograph Acknowledgments

Table of Contents

To the Reader

A high school senior expressed her feeling about life in these words:

Don't look;
You might see.
Don't think;
You might learn.
Don't walk;
You might stumble.

> Don't run;
> You might fall.
> Don't try;
> You might fail.
> Don't live;
> You might die.

This book is about people who prefer *Do* to *Don't*. In it you will read about the poor boy with an ugly scar on his face who will *do* what so many doubt he can do—go to the sun for the sake of the beautiful girl he loves; about the scrawny little man who will *do* what the crowd is sure he won't do—tackle the burly bear in a wrestling match; about a determined group of city boys who will *do* what even they themselves don't think they can do—turn a sooty city roof into a beautiful lawn.

You will also read the true story of Johnny Gunther, who knows he is dying but who strives nevertheless for good grades at school so he can enter the college of his dreams; about the adventures of Nellie Bly, who schemes around the clock for a way to enter the all-male world of the newspaper reporter; about the struggles of Levi Strauss, a penniless immigrant who makes his fortune.

You may wonder, as you read, why people strive for goals that seem strange. Why does a boxing champion quit the ring just when he can cash in on his title? Is he striving to act with a deeper kind of courage? Why does a young boy stay under water till his nose bleeds and his heart pounds and his lungs nearly burst? To swim from one end of a tunnel to another? Yes, it is that. And yet, it is more.

As Langston Hughes says in "Mother to Son":

> . . . all the time
> I'se been a-climbin' on,
> And reachin' landin's,
> And turnin' corners,
> And sometimes goin' in the dark
> Where there ain't been no light.
> So boy, don't you turn back.
> Don't you set down on the steps
> Cause you finds it's kinder hard.
> Don't you fall now—
> For I'se still goin', honey,
> I'se still climbin',
> And life for me ain't been no crystal stair.

Charles G. Spiegler

SCARFACE

by George Bird Grinnell

In the earliest times there was no war. All the tribes were at peace. In those days there was a man who had a daughter, a very beautiful girl. Many young men wanted to marry her, but every time she was asked, she only shook her head and said she did not want a husband.

"How is this?" asked her father. "Some of these young men are rich, handsome, and brave."

"Why should I marry?" replied the girl. "I have a rich father and mother. Our lodge is good. The parfleches are never empty. There are plenty of tanned robes and soft furs for winter. Why worry me, then?"

The Raven Bearers held a dance; they all dressed carefully and wore their ornaments, and each one tried to dance the best. Afterwards some of them asked for this girl, but still she said no. Then the Bulls, the Kit-foxes, and others of the *I-kun-uh'-kah-tsi* held their dances, and all those who were rich, many great warriors, asked this man for his daughter, but to every one of them she said no. Then her father was angry, and said: "Why, now, this way? All the best men have asked for you, and still you say no. I believe you have a secret lover."

"Father! mother!" replied the girl, "Pity me. I have no secret lover, but now hear the truth. That Above Person, the Sun, told me, 'Do not marry any of those men, for you are mine; thus you shall be happy, and live to great age'; and again he said, 'Take heed. You must not marry. You are mine.'"

"Ah!" replied her father. "It must always be as he says." And they talked no more about it.

There was a poor young man, very poor. His father, mother, all his relations, had gone to the Sand Hills. He had no lodge, no wife to tan his robes or sew his moccasins. He stopped in one lodge today, and tomorrow he ate and slept in another; thus he lived. He was a good-looking young man, except that on his cheek he had a scar, and his clothes were always old and poor.

After those dances some of the young men met this poor Scarface, and they laughed at him, and said: "Why don't you ask that girl to marry you? You are so rich and handsome!" Scarface did not laugh; he replied: "Ah! I will do as you say. I will go and ask her." All the young men thought this was funny. They laughed a great deal. But Scarface went down by the river. He waited by the river, where the women came to get water, and by and by the girl came along. "Girl," he said, "wait. I want to speak with you. Not as a designing person do I ask you, but openly where the Sun looks down, and all may see."

"Speak then," said the girl.

"I have seen the days," continued the young man. "You have refused those who are young, and rich, and brave. Now, today, they laughed and said to me, 'Why do you not ask her?' I am poor, very poor. I have no lodge, no food, no clothes, no robes and warm furs. I have no relations; all have gone to the Sand Hills; yet, now, today, I ask you, take pity, be my wife."

The girl hid her face in her robe and brushed the ground

2

with the point of her moccasin, back and forth, back and forth; for she was thinking. After a time she said: "True. I have refused all those rich young men, yet now the poor one asks me, and I am glad. I will be your wife, and my people will be happy. You are poor, but it does not matter. My father will give you dogs. My mother will make us a lodge. My people will give us robes and furs. You will be poor no longer."

Then the young man was happy, and he started to kiss her, but she held him back, and said: "Wait! The Sun has spoken to me. He says I may not marry; that I belong to him. He says if I listen to him, I shall live to great age. But now I say: Go to the Sun. Tell him, 'She whom you spoke with heeds your words. She has never done wrong, but now she wants to marry. I want her for my wife.' Ask him to take that scar from your face. That will be his sign. I will know he is pleased. But if he refuses, or if you fail to find his lodge, then do not return to me."

"Oh!" cried the young man, "at first your words were good. I was glad. But now it is dark. My heart is dead. Where is that far-off lodge? Where the trail, which no one yet has travelled?"

"Take courage, take courage!" said the girl; and she went to her lodge.

Scarface was very sad. He sat down and covered his head with his robe and tried to think what to do. After a while he got up, and went to an old woman who had been kind to him. "Pity me," he said. "I am very poor. I am going away now on a long journey. Make me some moccasins."

"Where are you going?" asked the old woman. "There is no war; we are very peaceful here."

"I do not know where I shall go," replied Scarface. "I am in trouble, but I cannot tell you now what it is."

So the old woman made him some moccasins, seven pairs,

with parfleche soles, and also she gave him a sack of food, pemmican of berries, pounded meat, and dried back fat; for this old woman had a good heart. She liked the young man.

All alone, and with a sad heart, he climbed the bluffs and stopped to take a last look at the camp. He wondered if he would ever see his sweetheart and the people again. "*Hai'-yu!* Pity me, O Sun," he prayed, and turning, he started to find the trail.

For many days he travelled on, over great prairies, along timbered rivers and among the mountains, and every day his sack of food grew lighter; but he saved it as much as he could, and ate berries, and roots, and sometimes he killed an animal of some kind. One night he stopped by the home of a wolf. "*Hai-yah!*" said that one; "what is my brother doing so far from home?"

"Ah!" replied Scarface, "I seek the place where the Sun lives; I am sent to speak with him."

"I have travelled far," said the wolf. "I know all the prairies, the valleys, and the mountains, but I have never seen the Sun's home. Wait; I know one who is very wise. Ask the bear. He may tell you."

The next day the man travelled on again, stopping now and then to pick a few berries, and when night came he arrived at the bear's lodge.

"Where is your home?" asked the bear. "Why are you travelling alone, my brother?"

"Help me! Pity me!" replied the young man; "because of her words I seek the Sun. I go to ask him for her."

"I know not where he stops," replied the bear. "I have travelled by many rivers, and I know the mountains, yet I have never seen his lodge. There is some one beyond, that striped-face, who is very smart. Go and ask him."

The badger was in his hole. Stooping over, the young man shouted: "Oh, cunning striped-face! Oh, generous animal! I wish to speak with you."

"What do you want?" said the badger, poking his head out of the hole.

"I want to find the Sun's home," replied Scarface. "I want to speak with him."

"I do not know where he lives," replied the badger. "I never travel very far. Over there in the timber is a wolverine. He is always travelling around, and is of much knowledge. Maybe he can tell you."

Then Scarface went to the woods and looked all around for the wolverine, but could not find him. So he sat down to rest. "*Hai'-yu; Hai'-yu!*" he cried. "Wolverine, take pity on me. My food is gone, my moccasins are worn out. Now I must die."

"What is it, my brother?" he heard, and looking around, he saw the animal sitting near.

"She whom I would marry," said Scarface, "belongs to the Sun; I am trying to find where he lives, to ask him for her."

"Ah!" said the wolverine. "I know where he lives. Wait; it is nearly night. Tomorrow I will show you the trail to the big water. He lives on the other side of it."

Early in the morning, the wolverine showed him the trail, and Scarface followed it until he came to the water's edge. He looked out over it, and his heart almost stopped. Never before had any one seen such a big water. The other side could not be seen, and there was no end to it. Scarface sat down on the shore. His food was all gone, his moccasins worn out. His heart was sick. "I cannot cross this big water," he said. "I cannot return to the people. Here, by this water, I shall die."

Not so. His helpers were there. Two swans came swimming up to the shore. "Why have you come here?" they asked him. "What are you doing? It is very far to the place where your people live."

"I am here," replied Scarface, "to die. Far away, in my country, is a beautiful girl. I want to marry her, but she

5

belongs to the Sun. So I started to find him and ask for her. I have travelled many days. My food is gone. I cannot go back. I cannot cross this big water, so I am going to die."

"No," said the swans; "it shall not be so. Across this water is the home of that Above Person. Get on our backs, and we will take you there."

Scarface quickly arose. He felt strong again. He waded out into the water and lay down on the swans' backs, and they started off. Very deep and black is that fearful water. Strange people live there, mighty animals which often seize and drown a person. The swans carried him safely, and took him to the other side. Here was a broad hard trail leading back from the water's edge.

"*Kyi*," said the swans. "You are now close to the Sun's lodge. Follow that trail, and you will soon see it."

Scarface started up the trail, and pretty soon he came to some beautiful things, lying in it. There was a war shirt, a shield, and a bow and arrows. He had never seen such pretty weapons; but he did not touch them. He walked carefully around them, and travelled on. A little way further on, he met a young man, the handsomest person he had ever seen. His hair was very long, and he wore clothing made of strange skins. His moccasins were sewn with bright colored feathers. The young man said to him, "Did you see some weapons lying on the trail?"

"Yes," replied Scarface; "I saw them."

"But did you not touch them?" asked the young man.

"No; I thought some one had left them there, so I did not take them."

"You are not a thief," said the young man. "What is your name?"

"Scarface."

"Where are you going?"

"To the Sun."

6

"My name," said the young man, "is A-pi-su-ahts.[1] The Sun is my father; come, I will take you to our lodge. My father is not now at home, but he will come in at night."

Soon they came to the lodge. It was very large and handsome; strange medicine animals were painted on it. Behind, on a tripod, were strange weapons and beautiful clothes—the Sun's. Scarface was ashamed to go in, but Morning Star said, "Do not be afraid, my friend; we are glad you have come."

They entered. One person was sitting there, Ko-ko-mik'-e-is,[2] the Sun's wife, Morning Star's mother. She spoke to Scarface kindly, and gave him something to eat. "Why have you come so far from your people?" she asked.

Then Scarface told her about the beautiful girl he wanted to marry. "She belongs to the Sun," he said. "I have come to ask him for her."

When it was time for the Sun to come home, the Moon hid Scarface under a pile of robes. As soon as the Sun got to the doorway, he stopped, and said, "I smell a person."

"Yes, father," said Morning Star; "a good young man has come to see you. I know he is good, for he found some of my things on the trail and did not touch them."

Then Scarface came out from under the robes, and the Sun entered and sat down. "I am glad you have come to our lodge," he said. "Stay with us as long as you think best. My son is lonesome sometimes; be his friend."

The next day the Moon called Scarface out of the lodge, and said to him: "Go with Morning Star where you please, but never hunt near that big water; do not let him go there. It is the home of great birds which have long sharp bills; they kill people. I have had many sons, but these birds have killed them all. Morning Star is the only one left."

So Scarface stayed there a long time and hunted with

[1] Early Riser, or Morning Star
[2] Night red light, or Moon

Morning Star. One day they came near the water, and saw the big birds.

"Come," said Morning Star; "let us go and kill those birds."

"No, no!" replied Scarface; "we must not go there. Those are very terrible birds; they will kill us."

Morning Star would not listen. He ran towards the water, and Scarface followed. He knew that he must kill the birds and save the boy. If not, the Sun would be angry and might kill him. He ran ahead and met the birds, which were coming towards him to fight, and killed every one of them with his spear; not one was left. Then the young men cut off their heads, and carried them home. Morning Star's mother was glad when they told her what they had done, and showed her the birds' heads. She cried, and called Scarface "my son." When the Sun came home at night, she told him about it, and he too was glad. "My son," he said to Scarface, "I will not forget what you have this day done for me. Tell me now, what can I do for you?"

"*Hai'-yu*," replied Scarface. "*Hai'-yu*, pity me. I am here to ask you for that girl. I want to marry her. I asked her, and she was glad; but she says you own her, that you told her not to marry."

"What you say is true," said the Sun. "I have watched the days, so I know it. Now, then, I give her to you; she is yours. I am glad she has·been wise. I know she has never done wrong. The Sun pities good women. They shall live a long time. So shall their husbands and children. Now you will soon go home. Let me tell you something. Be wise and listen: I am the only chief. Everything is mine. I made the earth, the mountains, prairies, rivers, and forests. I made the people and all the animals. This is why I say I alone am the chief. I can never die. True, the winter makes me old and weak, but every summer I grow young again."

Then said the Sun: "What one of all animals is smartest? The raven is, for he always finds food. He is never hungry.

Which one of all the animals is most Nat-ó-ye? [3] The buffalo is. Of all animals, I like him best. He is for the people. He is your food and your shelter. What part of his body is sacred? The tongue is. That is mine. What else is sacred? Berries are. They are mine too. Come with me and see the world." He took Scarface to the edge of the sky, and they looked down and saw it. It is round and flat, and all around the edge is the jumping-off place [or walls straight down]. Then said the Sun: "When any man is sick or in danger, his wife may promise to build me a lodge, if he recovers. If the woman is pure and true, then I will be pleased and help the man. But if she is bad, if she lies, then I will be angry. You shall build the last lodge like the world, round, with walls, but first you must build a sweat house of a hundred sticks. It shall be like the sky [a hemisphere], and half of it shall be painted red. That is me. The other half you will paint black. That is the night."

Further said the Sun: "Which is the best, the heart or the brain? The brain is. The heart often lies, the brain never." Then he told Scarface everything about making the Medicine Lodge, and when he had finished, he rubbed a powerful medicine on his face, and the scar disappeared. Then he gave him two raven feathers, saying: "These are the sign for the girl, that I give her to you. They must always be worn by the husband of the woman who builds a Medicine Lodge."

The young man was now ready to return home. Morning Star and the Sun gave him many beautiful presents. The Moon cried and kissed him, and called him "my son." Then the Sun showed him the short trail. It was the Wolf Road (Milky Way). He followed it, and soon reached the ground.

It was a very hot day. All the lodge skins were raised, and the people sat in the shade. There was a chief, a very generous man, and all day long people kept coming to his lodge to

[3] "Having Sun power," or Sacred

feast and smoke with him. Early in the morning this chief saw a person sitting out on a butte near by, close wrapped in his robe. The chief's friends came and went, the sun reached the middle, and passed on, down towards the mountains. Still this person did not move. When it was almost night, the chief said: "Why does that person sit there so long? The heat has been strong, but he has never eaten nor drunk. He may be a stranger; go and ask him in."

So some young men went up to him, and said: "Why do you sit here in the great heat all day? Come to the shade of the lodges. The chief asks you to feast with him."

Then the person arose and threw off his robe, and they were surprised. He wore beautiful clothes. His bow, shield, and other weapons were of strange make. But they knew his face, although the scar was gone, and they ran ahead, shouting, "The scarfaced poor young man has come. He is poor no longer. The scar on his face is gone."

All the people rushed out to see him. "Where have you been?" they asked. "Where did you get all these pretty things?" He did not answer. There in the crowd stood that young woman; and taking the two raven feathers from his head, he gave them to her, and said: "The trail was very long, and I nearly died, but by those helpers, I found his lodge. He is glad. He sends these feathers to you. They are the sign."

Great was her gladness then. They were married, and made the first Medicine Lodge, as the Sun had said. The Sun was glad. He gave them great age. They were never sick. When they were very old, one morning, their children said: "Awake! Rise and eat." They did not move. In the night, in sleep, without pain, their shadows had departed for the Sand Hills.

To James

by Frank Horne

Do you remember
How you won
That last race . . . ?
How you flung your body
At the start . . .
How your spikes
Ripped the cinders
In the stretch
How you catapulted
Through the tape . . .
Do you remember . . . ?
Don't you think
I lurched with you
Out of those starting holes . . . ?
Don't you think
My sinews tightened

At those first
Few strides . . .
And when you flew into the stretch
Was not all my thrill
Of a thousand races
In your blood . . . ?
At your final drive
Through the finish line
Did not my shout
Tell of the
Triumphant ecstasy
Of victory . . . ?
Live
As I have taught you
To run, Boy—
It's a short dash
Dig your starting holes
Deep and firm
Lurch out of them
Into the straightaway
With all the power
That is in you
Look straight ahead
To the finish line
Think only of the goal
Run straight
Run high
Run hard
Save nothing
And finish
With an ecstatic burst
That carries you
Hurtling
Through the tape
To victory . . .

MOTHER TO SON

by Langston Hughes

Well, son, I'll tell you:
Life for me ain't been no crystal stair.
It's had tacks in it,
And splinters,
And boards torn up,
And places with no carpet on the floor—
Bare.
But all the time
I'se been a-climbin' on,
And reachin' landin's,
And turnin' corners,
And sometimes goin' in the dark
Where there ain't been no light.
So boy, don't you turn back.
Don't you set down on the steps
'Cause you finds it's kinder hard.
Don't you fall now—
For I'se still goin', honey,
I'se still climbin',
And life for me ain't been no crystal stair.

Through the Tunnel

by Doris Lessing

Going to the shore on the first morning of the holiday, the young English boy stopped at a turning of the path and looked down at a wild and rocky bay, and then over to the crowded beach he knew so well from other years. His mother walked on in front of him, carrying a bright-striped bag in one hand. Contrition sent him running after her. And yet, as he ran, he looked back over his shoulder at the wild bay; and all morning, as he played on the safe beach, he was thinking of it.

Next morning, his mother said, "Are you tired of the usual beach, Jerry? Would you like to go somewhere else?"

"Oh, no!" he said quickly. Yet, walking down the path with her, he blurted out, "I'd like to go and have a look at those rocks down there."

It was a wild-looking place, and there was no one there, but she said, "Of course, Jerry. When you've had enough, come to the big beach." He almost ran after her again, feeling it unbearable that she should go by herself, but he did not.

Once Jerry saw that his mother had gained her beach, he

began the steep descent to the bay. As he ran sliding and scraping down the last few yards, he saw an edge of white surf, and the shallow, luminous movement of water over white sand, and, beyond that, a solid, heavy blue.

He ran straight into the water and began swimming. He was a good swimmer. When he was so far out that he could

16

look back not only on the little bay but past the promontory
that was between it and the big beach, he floated on the
buoyant surface and looked for his mother. There she was,
a speck of yellow under an umbrella that looked like a slice
of orange peel. He swam back to shore, relieved at being
sure she was there, but all at once very lonely.

On the edge of a small cape that marked the side of the bay away from the promontory was a loose scatter of rocks. Above them some boys were stripping off their clothes. They came running, naked, down to the rocks. The English boy swam towards them, and kept his distance at a stone's throw. They were of that coast, all of them burned smooth dark brown, and speaking a language he did not understand. To be with them, of them, was a craving that filled his whole body. He swam a little closer; they turned and watched him with narrowed, alert dark eyes. Then one smiled and waved. It was enough. In a minute, he had swum in and was on the rocks beside them, smiling with a desperate, nervous supplication. They shouted cheerful greetings at him, and then proceeded to forget him. But he was happy. He was with them.

Soon the biggest of the boys poised himself, shot down into the water, and did not come up. The others stood about, watching. After a long time the boy came up on the other side of a big dark rock, letting the air out of his lungs in a sputtering gasp and a shout of triumph. Immediately, the rest of them dived in. One moment, the morning seemed full of chattering boys; the next, the air and the surface of the water were empty. But through the heavy blue, dark shapes could be seen moving and groping.

Then one, and then another of the boys came up on the far side of the barrier of rock, and he understood that they had swum through some gap or hole in it. He plunged down. He could see nothing through the stinging salt water but the blank rock. When he came up, the boys were all on the diving rock, preparing to attempt the feat again. And now, in a panic of failure, he yelled up, in English, "Look at me! Look!" and he began splashing and kicking in the water like a foolish dog.

They looked down gravely, frowning. He knew the frown. At moments of failure, when he clowned to claim his mother's attention, it was with just this grave, embarrassed inspection that she rewarded him.

Water surged into his mouth; he choked, sank, came up. They were flying down past him, now, into the water; the air was full of falling bodies. Then the rock was empty in the hot sunlight. He counted one, two, three . . .

At fifty, he was terrified. They must all be drowning beneath him, in the watery caves of the rock! At a hundred, he stared around him at the empty hillside, wondering if he should yell for help. And then, at a hundred and sixty, the water beyond the rock was full of boys blowing like brown whales. They swam back to the shore without a look at him.

He climbed back to the diving rock and sat down, feeling the hot roughness of it under his thighs. The boys were gathering up their bits of clothing and running off along the shore to another promontory. They were leaving to get away from him. He cried openly, fists in his eyes. There was no one to see him, and he cried himself out.

It seemed to him that a long time had passed, and he went back to the villa to wait for his mother. Soon she walked slowly up the path, swinging her striped bag. "I want some swimming goggles," he panted.

He nagged and pestered until she went with him to a shop. As soon as she had bought the goggles, he grabbed them from her hand and was off, running down the steep path to the bay.

Jerry swam out to the big barrier rock. He fixed the goggles tight and firm, filled his lungs, and floated, face down on the water. Now he could see. It was as if he had eyes of a different kind—fish-eyes that showed everything clear and delicate and wavering in the bright water.

Under him, six or seven feet down, was a floor of perfectly clean, shining white sand, rippled firm and hard by the tides. Myriads of minute fish, the length of his fingernail, were drifting through the water, and in a moment he could feel the innumerable tiny touches of them against his limbs. It was like swimming in flaked silver. The great rock the big boys had swum through rose sheer out of the white sand, black, tufted lightly with greenish weed. He could see no gap in it. He swam down to its base.

Again and again he rose, took a big chestful of air, and went down. Again and again he groped over the surface of the rock. And then, while he was clinging to the black wall, his knees came up and he shot his feet out forward and they met no obstacle. He had found the hole. It was an irregular, dark gap, but he could not see deep into it. He clung with his hands to the edges of the hole, and tried to push himself in.

He got his head in, found his shoulders jammed, moved them in sidewise, and was inside as far as his waist. He could see nothing ahead. Something soft and clammy touched his mouth, he saw a dark frond moving against the greyish rock, and panic filled him. He thought of octopuses, of clinging weed. He pushed himself out backward and caught a glimpse, as he retreated, of a harmless tentacle of seaweed drifting in the mouth of the tunnel. But it was enough. He reached the sunlight, swam to shore, and lay on the diving rock. He looked down into the blue well of water. He knew he must find his way through that cave, or hole, or tunnel, and out the other side.

First, he thought, he must learn to control his breathing. He let himself down into the water with a big stone in his arms, so that he could lie effortlessly on the bottom of the sea. He counted. One, two, three. He counted steadily. He could hear the movement of blood in his chest. Fifty-one, fifty-two . . . His chest was hurting. He let go of the rock and went up into the air. He saw that the sun was low. He rushed to the villa and found his mother at her supper. She said only "Did you enjoy yourself?" and he said "Yes."

All night, the boy dreamed of the water-filled cave in the

rock, and as soon as breakfast was over he went to the bay.

That night, his nose bled badly. For hours he had been underwater, learning to hold his breath, and now he felt weak and dizzy. His mother said, "I shouldn't overdo things, darling, if I were you."

That day and the next, Jerry exercised his lungs as if everything, the whole of his life, all that he would become, depended upon it. And again his nose bled at night, and his mother insisted on his coming with her the next day.

A day's rest, he discovered, had improved his count by ten. The big boys had made the passage while he counted a hundred and sixty. He had been counting fast, in his fright. Probably now, if he tried, he could get through that long tunnel, but he was not going to try yet. A curious, most unchildlike persistence, a controlled impatience, made him wait. He sat by the clock in the villa, when his mother was not near, and checked his time. He was incredulous and then proud to find he could hold his breath without strain for two minutes.

In another four days, his mother said casually one morning, they must go home. On the day before they left, he would do it. He would do it if it killed him, he said defiantly to himself. But two days before they were to leave—a day of triumph when he increased his count by fifteen—his nose bled so badly that he turned dizzy and had to lie limply over the big rock like a bit of seaweed, watching the thick red blood flow on to the rock and trickle slowly down to the sea. He was frightened. He thought he would return to the house and lie down, and next summer, perhaps, when he had another year's growth in him,—*then* he would go through the hole.

But even after he had made the decision, or thought he had, he found himself sitting up on the rock and looking down into the water, and he knew that now, this moment, when his nose had only just stopped bleeding, when his head was still sore and throbbing—this was the moment when he would try. If he did not do it now, he never would.

He put on his goggles, fitted them tight, tested the vacuum. His hands were shaking. Then he chose the biggest stone he could carry and slipped over the edge of the rock until half of him was in the cool, enclosing water and half in the hot sun. He looked up once at the empty sky, filled his lungs once, twice, and then sank fast to the bottom with the stone. He let it go and began to count. He took the edges of the hole in his hands and drew himself into it, wriggling his shoulders in sidewise as he remembered he must, kicking himself along with his feet.

Soon he was clear inside. He was in a small rock-bound hole filled with yellowish-grey water. The water was pushing him up against the roof. The roof was sharp and pained his back. He pulled himself along with his hand—fast, fast —and used his legs as levers. His head knocked against something; a sharp pain dizzied him. Fifty, fifty-one, fifty-two . . . He was without light, and the water seemed to press upon him with the weight of rock. Seventy-one, seventy-two . . . There was no strain on his lungs. He felt like an inflated balloon, his lungs were so light and easy, but his head was pulsing.

A hundred, a hundred and one . . . The water paled. Victory filled him. His lungs were beginning to hurt. A few more strokes and he would be out. He was counting wildly; he said a hundred and fifteen, and then, a long time later, a hundred and fifteen again. The water was a clear jewel-green all around him. Then he saw, above his head, a crack running up through the rock. Sunlight was falling through it, showing the clean dark rock of the tunnel, a single mussel shell, and darkness ahead.

He was at the end of what he could do. He looked up at the crack as if it were filled with air and not water, as if he could put his mouth to it to draw in air. A hundred and fifteen, he heard himself say inside his head—but he had said that long ago. He must go into the blackness ahead, or he would drown. His head was swelling, his lungs cracking. A hundred and fifteen, a hundred and fifteen pounded through his head, and he feebly clutched at rocks in the dark, pulling himself forward, leaving the brief space of sunlit water behind. He felt he was dying. He struggled on in the darkness between lapses of unconsciousness. An immense, swelling pain filled his head, and then the darkness cracked with an explosion of green light. His hands, groping forward, met nothing, and his feet kicking back, propelled him out into the open sea.

He drifted to the surface, his face turned up to the air. He was gasping like a fish. He felt he would sink now and drown; he could not swim the few feet back to the rock. Then he was clutching it and pulling himself up on to it. He lay face down, gasping. He could see nothing but a red-veined, clotted dark. His eyes must have burst, he thought; they were full of blood. He tore off his goggles and a gout of blood went into the sea. His nose was bleeding, and the blood had filled the goggles.

He scooped up handfuls of water from the cool, salty sea, to splash on his face, and did not know whether it was blood or salt water he tasted. After a time, his heart quieted, his eyes cleared, and he sat up. He could see the local boys diving and playing half a mile away. He did not want them. He wanted nothing but to get back home and lie down.

In a short while, Jerry swam to shore and climbed slowly up the path to the villa. He flung himself on his bed and slept, waking at the sound of feet on the path outside. His mother was coming back. He rushed to the bathroom, thinking she must not see his face with bloodstains, or tearstains, on it. He came out of the bathroom and met her as she walked into the villa, smiling, her eyes lighting up.

"Have a nice morning?" she asked, laying her hand on his warm brown shoulder a moment.

"Oh, yes, thank you," he said.

"You look a bit pale." And then, sharp and anxious, "How did you bang your head?"

"Oh, just banged it," he told her.

They sat down to lunch together.

"Mummy," he said, "I can stay under water for two minutes —three minutes, at least." It came bursting out of him.

"Can you, darling?" she said. "Well, I shouldn't overdo it. I don't think you ought to swim any more today."

She was ready for a battle of wills, but he gave in at once. It was no longer of the least importance to go to the bay.

The Wonderful Lousy Poem

by Budd Schulberg

When I was eight or nine years old, I wrote my first poem.

At that time my father was a Hollywood tycoon, head of Paramount Studio. My mother was a founder and prime mover in various intellectual projects, helping to bring "culture" to the exuberant Hollywood community of the 1920's.

My mother read the little poem and began to cry. "Buddy, you didn't really write this beautiful, beautiful poem!" Shyly, proud-bursting, I stammered that I had. My mother poured out her welcome praise. Why, this poem was nothing short of genius. She had no idea that I had such talent for writing. I must write more poems, keep on writing, perhaps someday even publish them.

I glowed. "What time will Father be home?" I asked. I could hardly wait to show him what I had accomplished. My mother said she hoped he would be home around seven. I spent the best part of that afternoon preparing for his arrival.

First, I wrote the poem out in my finest flourish. Then I used colored crayons to draw an elaborate border around it that would do justice to its brilliant content. Then I waited. As seven o'clock drew near, I confidently placed it right on my father's plate on the dining-room table.

But my father did not return at seven. I rearranged the poem so it would appear at a slightly more advantageous angle on his plate. Seven-fifteen. Seven-thirty. The suspense was exquisite. I admired my father. I liked to go to the studio and watch the rough cut of his new pictures in his big projection room. And sometimes he would let me sit in when his important writers came to the house for story conferences. He had begun his motion-picture career as a writer. He would be able to appreciate this wonderful poem of mine even more than my mother.

Sometimes our household was like a Hollywood version of "Life with Father." It seemed as if the studio personnel were engaged in a great conspiracy to exhaust my father's patience. For instance, I never thought of movie stars simply as movie stars. I was accustomed to hearing them described as "those blank blank sons of blank stars!" Gloria Swanson, Marlene Dietrich, the formidable director Von Sternberg; the bigger they were, the more violent my father's denunciation.

This evening it was almost eight o'clock when my father burst in, and his mood seemed even more thunderous than usual. He was an hour late for dinner, but he could not sit down. He circled the long dining-room table with a Scotch highball in his hand, calling down terrible oaths on his glamorous employees. I can see him now, a big Havana cigar in one hand, the rapidly disappearing highball in the other, crying out against the sad fates that had sentenced him to the cruel job of running a teeming Hollywood studio.

"Imagine, we would have finished the picture tonight," my father was shouting. "Instead that blank blank MORON, that blank blank BLANK suddenly gets it into her beautiful but empty little head that she can't play the last scene. So the whole company has to stand there at $1,000 a minute while this silly little BLANK, who's lucky she isn't behind the counter of a five-and-ten, walks off the set! Now I have to go down to her beach house tonight and beg her to come back on Monday. I may just strangle her instead and finish the picture with her stand-in doing her scenes with her back to the blank blank camera!"

My father always paced determinedly as he ranted against the studio greats, and now as he wheeled he paused and glared at his plate. There was a suspenseful silence. He was reaching for my poem. I lowered my head and stared down into my plate. I was full of anxious daydreams. How wonderful it would be if this very first work of mine drove away the angry clouds that now darkened my important father's face!

"What is *this?*" I heard him say.

"Ben, Buddy has been waiting for you for hours," my mother began. "A wonderful thing has happened. Buddy has written his first poem! And it's beautiful, absolutely amaz—"

"If you don't mind, I'd like to decide that for myself," Father said.

Now was the moment of decision. I kept my face lowered to my plate. It could not have taken very long to read that poem. It was only ten lines long. But it seemed to take hours. I remember wondering why it was taking so long. I could hear my father breathing. Then I could hear him dropping the poem back on the table again. I could not bear to look up for the verdict. But in a moment I was to hear it:

"I think it's lousy," my father said.

I couldn't look up. I was ashamed of my eyes getting wet.

"Ben, sometimes I don't understand you," my mother was saying. "This is just a little boy. You're not in your studio now. These are the first lines of poetry he's ever written. He needs encouragement."

"I don't know why," my father held his ground. "Isn't there enough lousy poetry in the world already? I don't know any law that says Buddy has to become a poet."

27

I forget what my mother said. I wasn't hearing so well because it is hard to hear clearly when your head is making its own sounds of crying. On my left, she was saying soothing things to me and critical things of my father. But I clearly remember his self-defense: "Look, I pay my best writers $2,000 a week. All afternoon I've been tearing apart their stuff. I only pay Buddy fifty cents a week. And you're trying to tell me I don't have a right to tear apart his stuff if I think it's lousy!"

That expressive vernacular adjective hit me over the heart like a hard fist. I couldn't stand it another second. Leaving untouched the chocolate soufflé, my favorite dessert, I ran from the dining room bawling. I staggered up to my room and threw myself on the bed and sobbed. When I had cried the worst of the disappointment out of me, I could hear my parents still quarreling over my first poem at the dinner table.

That may have been the end of the anecdote—but not of its significance for me. Inevitably the family wounds began to knit. My mother began talking to my father again. My father asked me whether I would like to go to a prize fight. This was his favorite recreation, and I learned at a tender age to value the prowess of our California champions. I even began committing poetry again, though of course I dared not expose it to my father.

A few years later I took a second look at that first poem, and reluctantly I had to agree with my father's harsh judgment. It was a pretty lousy poem. After a while, I worked up the courage to show him something new, a primitive short story written in what I fancied to be the dark Russian manner. My father thought it was overwritten but not hopeless. I was learning to rewrite. And my mother was learning that she could criticize me without crushing me. You might say we were all learning. I was going on twelve.

But it wasn't until I was at work on my first novel, a dozen years later, that the true meaning of that painful "first poem" experience dawned on me. I had written a first chapter, but I didn't think it was good enough. I wanted to do it over. My editor, a wise hand who had counseled O'Neill and Sinclair Lewis and William Faulkner, told me not to worry, to keep on going, the first chapter was fine. Keep writing, just let it flow, it's wonderful, he encouraged me. Only when it was all finished and I was in a triumphant glow of achievement did he take me down a peg. "That chapter may be a little weak at that. If I were you, I'd look at it again." Now, on the crest of having written a novel, I could absorb a sharp critical blow.

As I worked my way into other books and plays and films, it became clearer and clearer to me how fortunate I had been to have had a mother who said, "Buddy, did you really write this—I think it's wonderful!" and a father who shook his head no and drove me to tears with his, "I think it's lousy." A writer, in fact all of us in life, needs that mother force, the loving force from which all creation flows; and yet the mother force alone is incomplete, even misleading, finally destructive, without the father force to caution, "Watch. Listen. Review. *Improve.*"

Sometimes you find these opposing forces personified in your editors, your associates, your friends, your loved ones. But finally you must counterpoise these opposites within yourself: first, the confidence to go forward, to do, to become; second, to temper rampant self-approval with hard-headed, realistic self-appraisal, the father discipline that barges into your ivory tower and with a painful truth jars your reverie of creative self-glorification.

Those conflicting but complimentary voices of my childhood echo down through the years—*wonderful, lousy, wonderful, lousy*—like two powerful, opposing winds buffeting me. I try to navigate my little craft so as not to capsize before either. Between the two poles of affirmation and doubt, both in the name of love, I try to follow my true course.

SOMETIMES IN LIFE YOU HAVE TO TAKE A CHANCE

from Death Be Not Proud

by John Gunther

This is not so much a memoir of Johnny in the conventional sense as the story of a long, courageous struggle between a child and Death. It is not about the happy early years except in this brief introduction, but about his illness. It is, in simple fact, the story of what happened to Johnny's brain. I write it because many children are afflicted by disease, though few ever have to endure what Johnny had, and perhaps they and their parents may derive some modicum of succor from the unflinching fortitude and detachment with which he rode through his ordeal to the end.

He died on June 30, 1947, when he was seventeen, after an illness that lasted fifteen months. He would have entered Harvard last autumn had he lived.

I must try to give you a picture of him. He was a tall boy, almost as tall as I when he died, and skinny, though he had been plump as a youngster, and he was always worried about putting on weight. He was very blond, with hair the color of wheat out in the sun, large bright blue eyes, and the most beautiful hands I have ever seen. His legs were still tall hairy stalks without form, but his hands were mature and beautiful. Most people thought he was very good looking. Perhaps as a father I am prejudiced. Most people did not think of his looks, however; they thought of his humor, his charm and above all his brains. Also there was the matter of selflessness. Johnny was the only person I have ever met who, truly, never thought of himself first, or, for that matter, at all; his considerateness was so extreme as to be a fault.

There was that day after the first operation, the operation that lasted almost six hours, when Dr. Putnam thought it wise to tell him what he had. Johnny was too bright to be forestalled by any more myths or euphemisms. As delicately as if he were handling one of his own instruments of surgery, Putnam said quietly, "Johnny, what we operated for was a brain tumor."

Nobody else was in the room, and Johnny looked straight at him.

"Do my parents know this? How shall we break it to them?"

Then, some months later, when he seemed to be getting better, he felt the edge of bone next to the flap in the skull wound, and looked questioningly and happily at the doctor —a different doctor—then attending him. The doctor was pleased because the bone appeared to be growing back, but with a crying lack of tact he told Johnny, "Oh, yes . . . it's growing . . . but in the wrong direction, the wrong way."

Johnny controlled himself and said nothing until the doctor left the room. His face had gone white and he was sick with sudden worry and harsh disappointment. Then he murmured to me, "Better not tell Mother it's growing wrong."

Johnny was to undergo more than one terrible operation before the close of his short life. The first one took place on April 29, 1946. His eyes were stuck fast for two days after the operation, and he feared that he was blind.

Later on, when he felt a little better, he became unhappy about the school work he was missing. All during his battle for life—for he had a great will to live—Johnny was also striving to complete his studies so he could graduate from Deerfield and go on to college. It was his special dream to get into Harvard.

As Johnny struggled on, the tumor in his head kept growing larger, until it was about the size of a tennis ball sticking out of his head. His condition kept growing worse and, on July 17, 1946, the "bump" opened up and began to drip pus. Yet Johnny strove on—patient and brave and humorous.

Another ordeal Johnny had to endure was the special diet he had to stick to. His doctor said, among other things, he could have nothing canned, seasoned, smoked, or frozen.

Neither was he allowed to have meat, fish, eggs, candy, sugar, ice cream, cake, butter or other fats. Of course, Johnny hated this diet, but he kept to it very strictly for it was part of his striving to stay alive. And as Johnny went on fighting to live and striving to learn, he never once gave in to a sense of defeat.

Now occurred the most remarkable of all remarkable things in the story of this struggle. Johnny accepted with disappointment but good spirit that he could not return to Deerfield—I broke the news to him—and he set out diligently to make up his lost school hours by tutoring. He could hardly walk without swaying; he could scarcely move his left fingers; he had lost half the sight of each eye; he was dazed with the poison from the bump; a portion of his brain had been eaten away; and yet he worked.

Frances found him two tutors and set them into their routine smoothly, while Johnny himself planned his daily endeavor like a general directing a battle. He helped map out the lessons himself, and knew with complete assurance and precision just what he wanted each tutor to cover in every session.

Here is a letter he wrote to the headmaster of Deerfield, as dictated to his mother:

November 4, 1946

DEAR MR. BOYDEN,

I am desperately worried about my work. Of last year's physics experiments I did exactly five out of thirty experiments due. Already I am far behind in chem. lab. I've forgotten every bit of French I ever knew, and there is this year's work, too. It is so *hard* to work when one's sick. My doctors, all twenty-three of them, agree that my tumor may have been growing six months or longer. Even in spring vacation my father noticed that I was very tired. I think that most of the year I was very tired, and I had a reputation for being "in a daze."

I am desperate and utterly miserable, since I don't see how I can ever catch up. My English marks were so terrible last year, too. It seems I'm going to stay in this hellish place forever. It's my birthday today (I'm seventeen). I'm going to Harvard next year (I hope) and there will be college boards—and final exams, this year's and last. It's absolutely a hopeless situation. I must implore you to persuade Mr. Haynes to forget about my physics lab, and Mrs. Boyden to excuse me of the chem. lab. that the other boys will have completed.

My English and French notes are lost, and I am desperate.

Please forgive me for unburdening myself in this way, and give my best to all the boys.

Yours very sincerely,

JOHN GUNTHER, JR.

P.S. You may tell Mr. Haynes that I did finally write up two experiments.
P.P.S. All this has been giving me acute and chronic neurasthenia.

Mr. Boyden, great gentleman that he is, not only replied cordially, but sent Mr. Haynes all the way into New York to give Johnny direct encouragement. Mr. Haynes had, I imagine, intended to stay only a moment or two, but he sat with Johnny hour after hour, and the visit helped his morale immensely.

Then Johnny wrote:

DEAR MR. BILL:

I would like very much to make an initial attempt at passing last year's final algebra exam. During the last month or two of vacation I was tutored in intermediate algebra by Mr. Elbert Weaver of Andover. We covered the whole year's work, especially what I was weak in—logarithms and trig. I am afraid that unless I take the exam very soon, I will for the second time forget all the algebra I ever knew.

Therefore I wish you would send an adequate examination to my father, so he may give it to me, under regular exam. conditions, in the time limits you may set.

I understand there will be no analytical geometry on the exam, but there will be the binomial theorem and factoring of cubes, all of which I have covered. We will send it back to you for correction, and I hope, if I don't do well on it, I may have another chance when I get back to school.

Please give my best to Mr. Boyden.

Then came a second letter to Mr. Boyden:

Nov. 20, 1946

Dear Mr. Boyden,

Thank you so much for your kind and considerate letter. My "neurasthenia" is gone and I am afraid that my letter was one of those that should have been written but never actually sent. I had an exceedingly nice talk with Mr. Haynes, and I am sure that I will be able to make up all the necessary work.

I am used to the diet now, and it really isn't at all bad. Every week I feel better and stronger.

I am trying to keep up nearly with my class in this year's history and English while tackling last year's exams one at a time, starting with algebra. Mrs. Boyden's subjects will be a pleasure any time I do them.

Came the great day when, under honor conditions, Johnny took a preliminary exam to see how well he would do. This was as much of a landmark as any in the whole course of the illness. One of his tutors thought he ought to wait, but there was no holding him. Johnny exclaimed, "Oh, Mother, tell him I want to get that test off my mind—and do the other things—my chemistry and physics—please *tell* him!" He repeated what had become a recurrent remark, with a strange, faraway look in his eyes (a "beyond" look, Frances called it). "You don't understand, Mother; I have so much to do, and there's so little *time!*" Finally the test was set for the next day, and he passed it satisfactorily. He commented then to Frances, "Sometimes in life you have to take a chance."

So he wrote:

Dec. 3, 1946

DEAR MR. HAYNES,

All my thanks for the things you sent. Against my tutor's advice, I took a three-hour trial exam (a N.Y. regents examination) in two hours, getting 77%. Consequently I don't think I will have any trouble with the one you sent.

The other day I listed forty-six chemical experiments that I have done in the last five or six years. I will write them up briefly in the hope that they will take care of my chemistry lab. for some time to come.

Best wishes to all.

It was after this that he made the mildly ironic comment, "Well, my tutors have finally caught up with me!"

Then he worsened sharply. The bump looked like two tomatoes and he became very tired and feverish, with the fever climbing uncomfortably high. Of course he had had some fever right along. Smears showed that staphylococci were present now, and this seemed to confirm Mount's worst fear, that infection of the meninges might occur. Putnam came back from California and paid a call. He was amazed that Johnny was still alive—let alone that he was well enough to take and pass examinations on schoolwork of the year before. Literally it seemed that Putnam could not believe his eyes, and he, Traeger, and Gerson talked most of an evening, behind closed doors, while Frances and I waited nervously upstairs, and Johnny dozed.

In December, 1946, Johnny was back in the hospital, where his tumor was drained. On January 12, 1947 he was back home with his worried parents.

Medically, the situation became more puzzling all the time. During March, Johnny was in good shape, though the bulge continued to grow very slowly and he had intermittent periods of seeming dazed and dopey and the hand and foot became somewhat worse and the lag in the mouth deepened. Also he was apt to drop things if he didn't watch his left hand. But the eyes were better. There was no recurrence of papilledema. How, we wondered, could he get better in one direction and worse in another, at one and the same time? We took him to an eye specialist who said that he did not think Johnny's eyesight would deteriorate further, and—blessed relief—that we need no longer fear blindness. But—suppose the partial numbness, the insidious creeping paralysis, should spread and so affect the right hand and foot in addition to the left? Some doctors said this was impossible. Others disagreed. If only the doctors would get together!

Straight through March and April, despite everything, Johnny worked on and on. He was utterly obsessed about getting into Harvard in the fall. But to achieve this he had to complete making up his work at Deerfield and graduate as well as pass the college entrance exams, a double task that seemed impossible. Then on March 18 we learned that he had caught up with his history course at Deerfield—though he hadn't been there for eleven months—and on

April 7 he had a letter from Mr. Boyden that gave him radiant happiness: he had passed his English examination satisfactorily and so was abreast of this course too. I took him to the science room in the Public Library, where he did some advanced work, and he proceeded to write up no fewer than fifty-four chemistry experiments! Then Frances found out about the New York Tutoring School, where Mr. Matthew is a wise and considerate headmaster, and we enrolled him there. Johnny's marks after six weeks were 90 in English, 95 in history, 95 in trig. This in a boy with half a brain!

We made formal application for him to enter Harvard, and in his own handwriting, now wretchedly uneven, he wrote the following paragraph to answer the question, "What are your reasons for going to college and why do you wish particularly to come to Harvard?"

I wish to go to college primarily to complete a sound general education and to prepare myself for the years to come. Also, I wish to prepare myself for research work in physical chemistry. I have chosen Harvard to atain (*sic*) these ends because I have been advised that it is the institution where I may most fruitfully attain these aims.

On April 12 he took the college board exams. It had been arranged, through the courtesy of Dean Gummere of Harvard, that he could split these into two sessions, taking the Aptitude tests at this time and the Achievement tests later. Johnny said he preferred to do both together, and who were we to say no to him? He announced, "I never felt better in my life." But it was a grueling day. We drove him down to a school near Gramercy Park early in the morning, and he had to wait almost an hour, standing mostly, in a huge milling crowd of tough, husky youngsters—many of them G.I.'s who had seen combat abroad—and then squeeze his way inch by inch into elevators packed and jammed, and run down long confusing corridors. A couple of the other boys laughed at him, and he flinched. Johnny looked so pitiably frail. His gait was lopsided, and his bandage made his pallor even more striking than it would have been otherwise. Frances kept close by. The exams lasted six and a half hours. We didn't get home till dinnertime, and Johnny flung himself on the couch, exclaiming, "Boy, *am* I tired!" Then he eagerly snapped to the phone to compare notes with other boys who had taken the same exams.

Johnny continued to study hard and to remain on the diet he loathed. Then on May 1, 1947, he was back in the hospital for another operation. His father said that it was one of the most terrible operations that a human being could undergo. Johnny suffered through it and, on May 15th, he was allowed to go home again. There was a faraway look in his eyes now, and all he had left was his will to live.

On Sunday mornings Frances read to him from the Hebrew Bible, the Christian Gospels, the Hindu scriptures, Confucius, and other eastern sages. One of the last things he read was the Psalms. I read to him, too, though not so much. One of the books he was going through for English was a poetry anthology; he would look bored or turn away whenever we chanced on a poem about Death.

One day came an unbearably moving moment when he announced, as if casually, that perhaps he was having the bump for *us!*

The phone rang on May 25 and Mr. Boyden's cheerful, assured voice came through. "I've gone through Johnny's papers and examinations," he said. "You know he did extra work in his freshman year and has some surplus credits. He has caught up to his class in everything except one examination, and we are going to give him a diploma. This isn't a favor. It is Johnny's right. Come up next week, and he will graduate with his class."

Johnny yawned and tried to look casual, and we all burst into tears.

We drove to Deerfield on May 27, and Johnny graduated on June 4, though he had not been to school for fourteen months. The days passed in a proud procession, and I think probably it was the happiest week of his life.

It seemed chilly when we started, and Johnny, as always extracting compensation out of any ill fortune, said, "Well, at least we don't have a heat wave." We passed through Hartford and he asked, "Were you here when you did your research?—I wouldn't dream of asking how long you stayed, probably half an hour." I was full of nerves as we got near Deerfield with its stiff old houses and great fanlike elms, and impatiently I asked him if I had overshot the side road and did he recognize any landmarks. He replied gently, "You know I don't see well out of my left eye."

Then without the slightest self-consciousness he took his place in his class. He sat between old friends in the dining hall (the instructors had warned them) and Frances whispered that they should inconspicuously cut his meat if necessary. The boys stared at him for a second as if he were a ghost—of course his hair had not grown back fully after the last operation and he wore a white turban—and then accepted his appearance without question.

Every evening after dinner an informal ceremony takes place at Deerfield which is one of the distinguishing marks of this magnificent school; each boy from Freshman to Senior meets with Mr. Boyden, and the roll of the entire school is called. The boys are heaped together on the floor. Usually there is a casualty or two—some youngsters hurt in a football game—for whom there are big leather chairs. Johnny eased himself into one of these, and his name was called in the roll exactly as if he had never been absent for a moment. Then he limped slowly and proudly to the

Senior Dorm where he would have been living this past year, and looked at what should have been his room with a piercing yearning. Boys were moving back and forth in the orderly bustle that precedes commencement. Johnny had the attitude of one who is both a participant in and a spectator of a great event. Mr. Boyden crept up to us and asked if we were sure he would not get too tired. Then he joined calmly in a bull session.

It was decided that he should sleep in the infirmary—a building he knew only too exasperatingly well. The next morning we came to pick him up at what we thought was a reasonable hour. But he had left the building before eight, alone, and was at that moment taking the final exam in chemistry! He passed it B Minus—though he had never taken a regular chemistry course in his life.

Later that day I bumped into him accidentally on the bright sunlit grass as he dragged himself from behind a hedge in shadow. His left shoulder sagged; his arm hung almost useless; his mouth was twisted with effort; the left side of his lip sank down; his eyes were filmy; he was happy. "Oh, pardon me, sir," Johnny said. He had not recognized me, and thought that I was some master he did not know.

Everybody tried hard to keep him from being too active. But he said, "Walking around this way helps the wound heal." Frances told him to sit around in the sun—how they both loved the sun!—and get brown and he answered, "All you are interested in, Mother, is my color!" When he had trouble with knife and fork one evening, he told her in exquisite parody of what she often said, "Be patient. Believe in calmness and Nirvana." It was a lovely day the next day and Johnny spent an hour learning some calculus from a fellow student. He worked out the equations on the bottom of a paper plate during a picnic lunch in the soft grass. Frances remonstrated that he might be getting tired. He replied briefly, "There's no future to just sitting."

The day before graduation was strenuous, with a lunch for the parents at noon and then a baseball game which Johnny watched with serious interest for about four innings. The dress-up banquet that night, to celebrate among other things Mr. Boyden's forty-fifth year as headmaster, lasted three hours; Johnny did not miss a minute of it. He tramped across the lawn afterward, with his classmate Henry Eisner holding his hand, for the off-the-record talk Mr. Boyden gives each graduating class. Then the class, standing under the trees in a night grown chilly, serenaded the Boydens on the front porch. Johnny, on the outskirts of the massed pack of boys, looked suddenly exhausted, and I slipped away from the adults to join him inconspicuously, standing just behind him. He did not mind, though as a rule he loathed having us anywhere near him at school. I was afraid he might fall. Then I heard his light, silvery tenor chime in with the other voices. The song floated across the lawn and echoed back. We hiked to the infirmary and Johnny ran into a classmate who had won an award. "Congratulations!" he snapped briskly.

The next morning the boys assembled early for the quarter-mile walk to the white-frame Deerfield church, arranging themselves four abreast in order of their height. I did not think Johnny could manage such a march. He shook us off and disappeared. The procedure is that the boys, reaching the church, line up behind the pews, and then walk one by one down the center aisle, as each name is called. Mr. Flynt, the president of the board of trustees, then shakes hands with each boy, giving him his diploma in the left hand. We explained that Johnny might not be able to grasp the smooth roll of diploma with his left fingers, and asked Mr. Flynt to try to slip it into the right hand instead. The boys began to march in slowly, and though Johnny should have been conspicuous with his white bandage, we did not see him and I was in an agony fearing that he had fallen out. Mr. Boyden, sweeping the assembly with his all-embracing sharp affectionate glance, caught Frances's eye and nodded to her reassuringly. One by one the names were called out, and each boy disassociated himself from the solid group and marched forward alone. The call was alphabetical, and by the time the G's were reached we were limp with suspense, since we did not know for sure that Johnny had even got into the church. As each boy passed down the aisle, there was applause, perfunctory for some, pronounced for others. Gaines, Gillespie, Goodwin, Griffin, Gunther. Slowly, very slowly, Johnny stepped out of the mass of his fellows and trod by us, carefully keeping in the exact center of the long aisle, looking neither to the left nor the right, but straight ahead, fixedly, with the white bandage flashing in the light through the high windows, his chin up, carefully, not faltering, steady, but slowly, so very slowly. The applause began and then rose and the applause became a storm, as every single person in that old church became whipped up, tight and tense, to see if he would make it. The applause became a thunder, it rose and soared and banged, when Johnny finally reached the pulpit, Mr. Flynt carefully tried to put the diploma in his right hand, as planned. Firmly Johnny took it from right hand to left, as was proper, and while the whole audience rocked now with release from tension, and was still wildly, thunderously applauding, he passed around to the side and, not seeing us, reached his place among his friends.

That evening we talked of Harvard. Some of the boys were getting their admission notices, and Johnny, now that he had actually been graduated, wondered when his would come. He was impatient. He had a great sense of the passage of time.

Everything that Johnny suffered was in a sense repaid by the few heroic moments of that walk down the center aisle of that church. This was his triumph and indomitable summation. Nobody who saw it will ever forget it, or be able to forget the sublime strength of will and character it took.

IT'S HER WAY

by Walter C. Meyer

The woods are full of folk singers these nights, and so are the cafes, coffee houses, college campuses and concert stages. With the exception of teen-geared, big-beat rockers, no other type of entertainer is growing in popularity with more people than the folk singer. But only a few are artists; among this elite is the unique Buffy Sainte-Marie. As a performer, her words, her tunes and her singing are different— she even looks different—from any other in the field. She is strictly her own woman—and her audiences love it. Which is why she's booked solid for appearances across the country, in Canada and abroad and is one of the top recording artists of this kind of music.

What makes the wholly self-taught Buffy uniquely herself is that she's a first-person musician. She writes the words and music for more than 90% of her material; for the rest she reworks folk traditionals so thoroughly they might as well be originals also. She sings in a clear, husky-timbred voice that can be sweet, low-down, bitter, compassionate, sprightly, sexy or wryly humorous. She can purr or belt, warm you into a smile or near chill you with a trembling intensity. Her guitar-playing is unorthodox, too. She taught

herself "all backwards," and her music often has "a strange flavor." To complete her unique performance, she dresses in colorful and exciting fashion—such as wearing exotic African gowns.

Another unusual fact: Buffy is an Indian, a copper-skinned, raven-haired 25-year-old of striking visage. Born to Cree parents just over the border in Saskatchewan, Canada, she was orphaned when an infant. A part-Indian couple named Sainte-Marie who had lost a baby of their own adopted her, named her Beverley (Buffy for short) and brought her up in Wakefield, Mass. Through them she gained American citizenship. Summers she lived with her family in a lakeside trailer near Naples, Maine. A shy child, she spent hours wandering through nearby woods and began to write poetry and, later, songs to fit the words. (Her song output now totals well over 200.)

When she entered the University of Massachusetts at Amherst, Buffy had no guitar, did not sing, was still shy and wanted to be a veterinarian. By graduation, by practicing long hours every day, she'd taught herself the guitar and how to sing, had acted in plays, done practice teaching, was an honor student, earned a B.A. degree in *two* majors, education and Oriental philosophy, and was voted one of the 10 outstanding seniors in the class of '63. She was also an experienced folk performer with a large following.

When she came to New York and guested at three hootenannys she was besieged with job and recording offers. She rejected them all and went back to the Maine woods for a couple of months to think things out. The offers followed, and in time, Buffy decided on a folk singing career and returned here.

Buffy's so much on the go that she has no real home of her own. If and when she does take a break, it's with relatives in Maine.

But Buffy's quick to say that her life is no rat race, that she does have time for a dozen hobbies, including writing a cookbook of original recipes, photography, ice-skating, archery, hunting, riding, painting, drawing tarot (fortune-telling) cards, the study of philosophy, religion and astrology, play- and movie-going and collecting unusual musical instruments. She does two or three of these at a time, she says, because "I can't sit still and I hate most to be bored."

Protest songs are favored by folk singers these days and again Buffy's angle is unique and personal. She's against Uncle Sam's treatment of the Indian. "One of my goals is to get people to know the full story about the Indians. I want to correct the image that movies, television and 'censored history books' have created. I resent this as an American and am terrified as an Indian that this should still exist."

One of her songs on this subject, "My Country 'Tis of Thy People You're Dying," still raises her hackles whenever she sings it and it's likely to raise a listener's, too—it's that searing. When she has finished it, Buffy's apt to tell the audience, with a shy smile, "I hope you're offended." In an effort to aid her people she has lectured on Indian problems.

As an Indian, the copper-toned Buffy has experienced racial discrimination in the past, but now that she's a name performer, she has no trouble.

"New York excites me," declares Buffy. "It's big and intense—it can be disgusting on Monday and thrilling on Tuesday. I hate its air, but I can create here as well as in a quiet place like Maine."

Buffy frankly admits she's thrilled by the attention she attracts. "It's all as exciting and glamorous as I imagined it would be—and twice as much work!" And some of that work comes not from "singing a song as pure music, note for note, but in striving to capture the essence of the song and give it to my listeners as a complete, totally new experience. I try to make something happen to my listeners."

If you get to hear and see Buffy Saint-Marie, you *could* get all shook up. It's her way.

from IT'S MY WAY

by Buffy Sainte-Marie

I'm cutting my own way,
Through my own day,
And all I dare say
Is it's my own.

I can tell you
Things I've done,
And I can sing you
Songs I've sung.

But there's one thing I can't give
For I and I alone can live
The years I've known
And the life I've grown,
Got a way I'm going
And it's my way.

Don't be sighing.
Don't be crying.
Your day will come.
Your day alone.

I've got my own joy.
I've got my own load.
I've got my own road.
And it's my way.

Put down the story,
Of what I've known.
You're bound for glory,
All of your own glory.
Glory, all of your own one day.

THE AGONY OF VICTORY

by George Spiegler

The boxing game is a rough business, a very rough business. For most fighters, boxing is a livelihood through which they scratch out a meager existence. A select few make it. Others end their careers as punchdrunk bums living in grotesque Bowery flophouses for the remainder of their lives. For some, fighting is the pot of gold at the end of the rainbow, the only hope for poverty–stricken slum boys. For others, it's cauliflower ears and kidneys pounded until they bleed. One former world champion is now a forty-three–year old shoe shine boy in a Miami hotel. Another is completely blind. Boxing promoters and managers are by-and-large ruthlessly inhuman. They maneuver for position in boxing's ugly jungle, even if it means sacrificing a fighter. Their main concern is the "buck."

George Bradford was aware of all of these things, but unafraid. Bradford, the Negro son of a Bronx truck driver, was a great middleweight prospect in the early 1950's, until fate overtook him. Although Georgie knew that boxing was a scandalously exploited sport, he was determined to fight his way out of the slums, to make a place for himself and his family in the world, and to become famous. He wanted glory. Nothing would stop him from attaining it.

This was no run-of-the-mill middleweight. This was a true sensation, a whirlwind boxer-puncher with an iron jaw. In addition to dazzling footwork and a fighting heart, Bradford possessed a stunning left jab, a tremendous left hook, and his "big" punch, a crunching, finishing right cross. These were not only powerful punches. They were accurate, precise bombs, which would pinpoint a target and, more often than not, find it. His defense was superb, already polished like a veteran's. The Bronx battler fought best when in trouble. When Georgie Bradford went down, Georgie Bradford got up. Undefeated in eighty-one fights as amateur and pro, he flattened two-thirds of his opponents, few of whom were soft touches. Georgie fought the best and beat the best. And he had class—not only as a fighter, but as a man.

In his first professional fight he knocked out Alonzo Scarponi with his second punch of the first round. He then flattened a host of other middleweights in quick succession. The interesting thing was that he never mocked or insulted his conquered opponents. He complimented them to the press and others.

After two years of continued success, the "Bronx Bomber," as the fight writers had begun to label him, fought Vince Jordan, number four ranking middleweight, in a nationally televised bout. And here, Bradford did something which is still talked about today, something which few fighters had ever done. Rocked badly by Jordan's first punch, Bradford came back to knock down his rival five times in round four, until Jordan was leaning against the ropes, utterly helpless. Georgie hit him with a dynamite right hand, and Jordan crashed to the floor with a thud. He lay still for a moment, and then began a pitiful struggle to lift himself from the canvas. Georgie knew that for Jordan the fight was over. Georgie appealed to the referee to stop the fight, but the "ref" refused. The crowd booed resentfully, flooding Bradford with a chorus of catcalls and insults. They forgot that Vince Jordan was in terrible pain. They didn't care. The referee wouldn't take it upon himself to stop the fight. So Bradford himself rose to the occasion and stopped the slaughter. As he left the ring, he heard a wrathful flood of abuse which he couldn't understand.

Deep within him, he began to feel his conscience gnawing at him. One voice within him insisted he should stop fighting because boxing was a savage, cold–blooded sport, while another told him to continue for the sake of his family. The newspapers were now applauding him as the next middleweight champ, the second coming of Walker. He was now number two contender for Jack Thompson's crown. Big money gates were in the making. Everyone wanted to see the new superman of the squared circle. His family had moved from its slum apartment into a much better neighborhood outside the city. Both Georgie and his family were living comfortably. All in all, the situation was favorable. Yet Georgie Bradford, professional boxer and number two contender for one of boxing's richest thrones, wasn't a happy person. Something was eating him. He didn't know what. But there was a great conflict within his heart. He began to feel that boxing wasn't worth it. He sensed that his efforts were being directed the wrong way. Essentially ethical, Georgie began to regard his occupation as authorized murder. He began to feel guilty deep inside. How could he forget that one more punch landed on Vince Jordan's head could very well have made him a killer? The thought horrified him.

But Bradford's manager, Mike Rickard, wanted another big "payday," so the Bronx Battler was matched with Rocky Johnson, number six ranking contender. Georgie accepted reluctantly. The newspapers stated that Johnson was in a class below Bradford's and that he wouldn't last beyond round five. But the fight was close, a split decision for Bradford. He couldn't hit Johnson for fear of seriously damaging him. He'd already terminated one career with his potent fists. Only a few months before, he had come perilously close to killing Vince Jordan, and he didn't want a repeat of that terrible incident.

In the dressing room after the fight, Rickard, fed up with his fighter, shouted, "What went wrong with ya tonight?" Georgie was silent. "Were you sick? Why didn't ya tell me?"

"Just had a bad night, I guess."

"O.K., but remember you go against Mitsunori Souleymanne next time. I've got him lined up for ya. You can't have a bad night with this guy. He's got a pretty good left hook. You stay away from that. But he's got a glass jaw, see. You beat this guy and the Thompson fight's a natural, 'cause he's Number One. Make sure you flatten him early. You'll kill him, Georgie. You'll murder the guy."

"I hope so, Mike. I'll try," answered Georgie. There was a note of sorrow in his voice. His own manager didn't understand what was going on inside him.

The fight was scheduled for December 14, 1954. The winner was promised a fight with Jack Thompson for the middleweight championship of the world. After two dull rounds, Souleymanne landed his vaunted left hook on Bradford's jaw. The Bronx fighter went down on a knee, as the crowd stood aghast. Up at seven, Georgie fell into a clinch to save himself until the cobwebs loosened. Then, with about a minute left in the round, Bradford cut loose with everything in his arsenal for the first time since the Jordan fight. Those sitting at home, listening on radio, heard this account of the battle from ring announcer Don Elliot:

The fighters are in midring now. It's been a cautious fight, so far. Should liven up though. Bradford throws a left jab, a left hook. Souleymanne is shaken. He falls into a clinch. Bradford pounds him loose with a tremendous left hook which doubles Souleymanne up. A right cross, a left, a crunching right hand! Souleymanne's in trouble! He's reeling on the ropes! Bradford at him like a tiger! He's not gonna let him go now! Murderous left hook, a crushing right to the jaw, another left, a bombing right! Souleymanne's slammed into the ropes! This could be it! Let's see! Bradford jumps in with a crashing left, a bombing right uppercut to the jaw! Souleymanne's gasping for breath. His right eye's completely closed! His left is swelling! He's on the ropes again! Bradford throws the right to the jaw, a bombing left hook to the stomach! Souleymanne's hanging on for dear life! Bradford's banging away like the Bradford of old! Murderous fusillades! Oh! Oh! A crashing left. Souleymanne is flat on his back! He's on the ring apron! He won't get up! Josephs sends Georgie to a neutral corner! He picks up the count. Three! Four! Five! Six! But wait, Souleymanne's getting up! This fight's not over yet! Seven! He's on a knee. But he falls back! Eight! Nine! He's dragging himself up again! He's . . . up! He makes it by a half-second! Will Josephs stop the fight? He's looking him over! Don't leave your seats! This fight's still on! Bradford charges from his corner! His right hand is cocked. He corners Souley-manne in his own corner. A murderous crash to the head! Souleymanne's face is a crimson red! The blood's pouring all over the ring! The crowd's cheering madly! They stand as a man and urge Georgie on! A left, a right, a left, a right and Souleymanne crashes to the floor, on his knees! His eyes are glazed! But he's getting up! He's battered with murderous combinations, left after left, to the side of his head! Bradford smashes him down again! If I've ever seen a slaughter, this is it! Souleymanne's face is a bloody hulk! He's flat on his stomach! He can't go on! I'm sure of it! He's unconscious! This fight is all over at 2:43 of the third round!

At first the crowd cheered. Then, there was silence. It took only a few minutes before everyone knew the truth—Souleymanne was dead.

His death was also the death of Georgie Bradford's great hopes. He would never fight again. Let his manager sign his papers for a Bradford-Thompson fight, $300,000. Let there be a $30,000 guarantee for a Bronx boy who had finally made it in the jungle; a boy who had hurdled all obstacles, dating back to a youth of discrimination and poverty; who through nothing but hard work and faith had climbed to the top of the world. Let people think he was the number one contender for the middleweight championship of the world. Let the newspapers make him a 4 to 1 favorite, hail him as the new champ, the greatest fighter of the decade. Georgie Bradford's career as a fighter was over. He gave all this up willingly.

Georgie wanted a future based on life, not on death. The newspapers, the boxing mob, even some of his close friends criticized Georgie severely for his decision. They didn't understand. They might have, if they'd taken time out to look not at Georgie Bradford as a professional boxer, but at Georgie Bradford as a man. Perhaps they would have understood had they noticed Georgie Bradford sit down on his stool about a minute after the fatal Souleymanne knockout, and cry quietly, silently to himself.

CAST LIST

CARRIE HAYES
A Supervisor of Nurses

GAIL LUCAS
A Nurse

JENNY BISHOP
A Nurse

JOSEPH BARBIROLLI
A Hospital Patient

MRS. HILL
Jenny's Aunt

LONNIE HILL
Jenny's Cousin

MR. SELIGMAN
A Hospital Administrator

FIRST CLEANING WOMAN

SECOND CLEANING WOMAN

THE NARRATOR

Express Stop from Lenox Avenue

by Adrian Spies

SCENE I

NARRATOR

> This is the story of Jenny Bishop, a young and successful Negro nurse who is succeeding so well at her job that she is being considered for a promotion. One day she is visited by her cousin and her aunt, neither of whom she is happy to see. Jenny thinks of Lonnie, her cousin, as "beneath" her. He has had little education and he is out of a job. Another thing Jenny dislikes about Lonnie is his goatee. Mrs. Emma Hill, her aunt, is a cleaning woman whose very presence in the hospital embarrasses Jenny. As the story opens we see and hear—

JENNY (*flustered, trying not to show it, but pitching her voice lower than necessary*)
> What are you two doing here?

MRS. HILL

> I'd just as soon *not* be, Jenny . . . If your cousin (*Indicating Lonnie.*) didn't need you, I wouldn't be . . .

LONNIE

All right, Ma . . . Don't start that jazz . . .

MRS. HILL

You shut up, Lonnie . . . She'd like to forget you and me, and what we did for her . . . I just wish we could afford to keep our pride and forget *her* . . .

JENNY (*still low, lower than necessary*)

I didn't forget you . . .

MRS. HILL

We took you in . . . We were half on relief ourself, but God saw to it and we took you in . . . My two brothers and me . . . We took turns, we took you in! And now, now (*Pointing contemptuously to a name tag on Jenny's dress.*) now, *Miss Bishop*, you never come around!

JENNY (*a whisper, humiliated that people could hear this*)

My hours are crazy, Auntie Emma . . . There's always a girl sick, and I fill in . . . And I send you checks, don't I? . . . Christmas, you got the checks?

LONNIE (*quick to agree*)

We got them, Jenny . . . Thank you very much . . .

MRS. HILL (*cold*)

Writing a check ain't hard, if you got a little money in the bank . . . What's hard is remembering who done for you when you needed it.

Jenny shakes her head helplessly. She knows she can't explain herself, her aspirations, to this woman. She looks at Lonnie.

JENNY

Lonnie, what is it? . . . Your mother says you need help . . .

LONNIE

Well, I guess I need a job, Jenny . . . (*With apologetic shrug.*) I worked for a cat, but he went out of business . . .

Jenny looks at him—the silly goatee, the well meaning but rather stupid face, a habit he has, a Harlem street corner habit, of doing an unconscious tap dance with one foot as he stands there. Jenny knows what they have in mind but she isn't admitting it to herself.

JENNY

I know a man, a builder . . . Maybe he could use somebody . . .

MRS. HILL

We don't need no man, no builder . . . Your cousin and me—we inquired downstairs . . . (*challengingly*) There's openings right here . . . for orderlies . . .

JENNY

Oh . . . (*After a pause, looking at them, particularly at the goatee, and then speaking.*) Well, I happen to know they're trying to—well, upgrade the orderly situation here . . . What I mean is, get people who— have better educations . . . (*Knowing Lonnie hasn't.*) At least a high school diploma . . .

LONNIE (*grinning*)

I mean to take night courses . . . I mean, when you talk about upgrade, you talking about me, Coz.

Again, he grins nervously. Again he taps his foot in a zooty, foolish style, again the goatee bobs.

MRS. HILL

You listen to me, Jenny . . . Blood to blood, listen to me . . . (*Coming closer to her.*) Lonnie already filled *out* an application downstairs . . . Some man there, he *mentioned* a high school diploma, but when we said Lonnie was your cousin, your first cousin, that seemed to mean a lot . . . (*After another pause, burning her eyes into Jenny's.*) You hear me, Jenny? Lonnie gave *you* as a reference . . . And don't you dare stand in your cousin's way! . . . Don't you dare turn your back on this boy!

Jenny stares into her aunt's fierce, cold face. Then turning, looking at Lonnie who, again, with the foolish reflex, is tapping one foot. Jenny nods. Of course she can't turn her back on this boy. And we see that in the confusion of mixed emotions on her face.

SCENE II (*Hospital cafeteria*)

Jenny comes in by herself—it is just a few moments since she had a scene upstairs with her aunt and cousin. She is upset. She gets some Jello and coffee and goes to a table from which Carrie, a supervisor of hospital staff, has waved to her.

JENNY
    Sorry I'm late . . .

CARRIE (*pointing to the food*)
    Never mind . . . It's not going to take you long to eat that!

Jenny shrugs indifferently, takes a tiny taste of the Jello. Carrie knows Jenny is troubled about something. Of course, there is nothing to be said.

    A man is passing their table now, having finished his meal. His name is Mr. Seligman—he's an administrative official in the hospital.

SELIGMAN

You're Miss Bishop, aren't you?

JENNY

That's right . . .

SELIGMAN (*smiling, sitting down*)

Well, I've just saved myself a trip upstairs . . . (*Fumbling in his pocket.*) I was on my way to check something with you . . . (*Getting a piece of paper out of his pocket now, looking at it.*) A fellow was around not long ago looking for a job as an orderly . . . (*Reading from the paper.*) Lonnie Jim Hill . . . He says he's your cousin, is that right?

Jenny can't help herself. She feels embarrassed, trapped. She's aware of Carrie.

JENNY (*softly*)

Yes . . .

SELIGMAN (*looking up, he didn't hear*)

What was that?

JENNY

Yes . . . We're—related . . .

Seligman nods. He looks down at the application form.

SELIGMAN

We're short . . . In that category, we're always short. He said he was going to go up and say hello to you.

JENNY (*again aware of Carrie, again embarrassed*)

He did . . .

CARRIE (*sensing Jenny's deep embarrassment*)

You two are talking business . . . I'll go ahead . . .

SELIGMAN (*he's missing all the nuances here*)

No, Miss Hayes . . . I want to ask *you* about the

61

department head meeting next week. I was going to do that upstairs, too . . . (*shrugging, smiling*) I guess I'm saving *two* trips . . . Anyway, I'll just take a second with Miss Bishop here.

Carrie doesn't know what to do. She's trapped, she sits there. Jenny feels trapped, too, by her own self-consciousness about Lonnie. She just sits there tensely.

SELIGMAN (*running his eye down the form*)
　　He seemed like a nice enough fellow, Miss Bishop . . .

JENNY (*strained*)
　　Yes . . . Though I—I really don't know him too well anymore . . .

SELIGMAN (*a little surprised, looking up*)
　　No?

JENNY
　　What I mean—I haven't seen him much for a long time.

SELIGMAN
　　But you *did* live with him and his mother? . . . I think he mentioned that . . .

JENNY
　　Yes but—(*Wavering, knowing there was really no need for buts, then going on weakly.*) Yes—a long time ago.

Seligman looks at her a little surprised, as though this was unnecessary. Then he looks down at the form. He frowns slightly.

SELIGMAN
　　He hasn't held any jobs too long . . .

JENNY (*as if she didn't know this*)
　　Oh?

SELIGMAN

And the type of jobs he *did* have—well, I guess you know, Miss Bishop, nothing too outstanding . . . Pin boy in a bowling alley, a five minute car wash—that's about the level . . .

JENNY (*tautly*)

Well, I'm not *defending* him, Mr. Seligman! . . . Or his vocational inadequacies, either!

SELIGMAN (*quickly as though apologizing*)

No . . . of course . . . I wouldn't expect you to.

For the first time, Mr. Seligman has some idea of Jenny's attitude. He's flustered, he fusses with his pipe.

SELIGMAN

I guess I got my signals crossed, Miss Bishop . . . I had the idea you had told your cousin to come see us . . .

JENNY

No . . . I didn't. (*She feels the need to go on. She knows she's fumbling things, but she goes on.*) The fact is, I don't believe in that . . . I mean—people using pull or anything, taking work away from some deserving person just because somebody they happen to be related to gets a notion . . . (*After a pause, feeling foolish.*) Oh, I didn't say that right . . . I just mean—

SELIGMAN (*quickly*)

Miss Bishop, I know exactly what you mean . . . And I agree . . . I agree one hundred per cent . . . But in this case—well, to tell you the truth, Miss Bishop, there *are* no other applicants right now . . . We're short on orderlies, and it was fine with me when your cou—(*Checking himself, sensing she doesn't want to hear Lonnie referred to that way.*) when this young

63

fellow came in and asked for a job . . . (*Shrugging.*) I might wish he had a little better work record, and a little better educational record too, for that matter, but I've just about decided to take him on . . . (*After a slight pause.*) That is, naturally, if you *do* give him a character reference . . .

Jenny just sits there. She looks down at the table, she knows she must say something. It's very, very hard.

JENNY (*strained, managing for it to come out grudging*)
> Well, I don't know anything wrong with his *character* . . .

SELIGMAN
> Well, good . . . Thank you very much . . . That's that . . .

Jenny can't sit there anymore. She stands up, very abruptly.

JENNY
> Excuse me. . . I've—got some things to do upstairs . . .

Seligman nods, smiles, so does Carrie. Jenny turns, quickly goes off. Mr. Seligman and Carrie look after her.

SELIGMAN
> Peculiar young lady . . . Doesn't seem to know what she wants. They're so difficult to talk to, aren't they? I mean, you can never tell what's going on in their minds.

CARRIE (*dryly*)
> It's funny . . . I have that trouble with everybody. Besides, Miss Bishop's a first-rate nurse. That's all I'm interested in.

SELIGMAN
> Oh, absolutely. I couldn't agree more. As a matter of fact, if I'm not mistaken her name's on a list of personnel recommended for advancement.

64

CARRIE

For my money, she deserves it.

SELIGMAN

Oh, I'm sure she does!

CARRIE

You take a good hard look at Jenny Bishop's file, Mr. Seligman, you'll find that way back when she was a student and I was her clinical instructor, I had no reservations as to her future as a nurse.

SELIGMAN

Good. I'm interested to hear that. Very interested indeed. We're on the lookout, you know . . . The neighborhood's changing, and more and more of our patients are . . . That's why we have to keep pace. Find the good ones and move them along. That's the thing, isn't it?

Carrie really despises this flannel-mouthed old milksop.

CARRIE

Oh, that's the thing all right. Well, you can't go wrong with Miss Bishop . . . I mean as long as you're keeping pace anyway.

She exits, leaving Mr. Seligman to look after her and to wonder what she meant by that last remark. Was that sarcasm? Had he said something to offend her? What a trial these people are . . .

SCENE III (*Utility room*)

Carrie and Lonnie enter. Lonnie is dressed in whites. He has just reported for his first day of floor duty and is being given a quick orientation tour by Carrie.

CARRIE

You with me so far?

LONNIE

Yes, ma'am.

CARRIE

Good. Now this is the utility room. Very important place in our little scheme of things.

LONNIE (*looking around*)

Yeah . . . this looks like the place all right.

CARRIE (*smiles, says casually*)

Pretty happy coincidence, getting your first practical training on the same floor as Jenny. It's going to be pretty confusing for a couple of days.

LONNIE

You know that's true.

CARRIE

So ask questions.

LONNIE

I won't be afraid . . . I know what to ask . . .

CARRIE (*with a smile*)

Don't worry about that.

She goes to where some equipment is stored. Lonnie's attitude throughout is attentive and reveals him to be taking this responsibility seriously.

CARRIE

We all do our best to keep things clean and ready for use, but it'll be your responsibility along with the aides to see to it that things are kept shipshape . . . but never forget that the patients come first . . . I think that does it . . . Any questions?

Lonnie looks blankly at her a moment, then grins shyly.

LONNIE

Yeah . . . where does an alien go to register?

CARRIE (*laughs, opens the door*)

Come on, alien . . . you haven't started yet!

She leads the way out followed by Lonnie.

SCENE IV (*Mr. Barbirolli's room*)

Jenny comes out of the elevator. She's wearing her cape, she's been out, and she carries a package. She's headed toward Mr. Barbirolli's room. But just as she's getting there, something down the hall distracts her, makes her look. She looks in a troubled way. We see what she's looking at. Lonnie, dressed in an orderly outfit now, is down the hall. He doesn't see her. We see clearly the way she feels—she wishes he weren't here.

Jenny turns, looks toward Mr. Barbirolli. He's looking toward her eagerly. She nods, smiles, indicates the package. We see her mood changing as she enters the room—this is what she likes, not thoughts about Lonnie, but this. She walks up to Mr. Barbirolli and hands him the package.

JENNY

Your friend in the book shop sent a great big hello to you . . .

Mr. Barbirolli nods, looks at the package eagerly, seems to pat it.

BARBIROLLI

Thank you, Miss Bishop . . . For wasting your lunch hour this way—lugging books for *me* . . .

JENNY

You know I enjoyed it . . .

Mr. Barbirolli looks up at her. He nods.

BARBIROLLI

Oh, knowing you, I'm sure you enjoyed it—my friend's

shop, the books, the good prints . . . But it still was a kindness, Miss Bishop . . .

JENNY (*pleased with this, a little flustered*)
Well, aren't you going to open it up? . . . I'm kind of curious myself to see all that heavy reading . . . (*Kidding, indicating the books were heavy by the way she holds her arms.*) And I do mean *heavy* . . .

Mr. Barbirolli smiles quickly, as if at her little joke. Then he looks down at the package, and there is a certain wistfulness in his manner.

BARBIROLLI
I guess I'll tease myself a while, Miss Bishop . . . Now that I have these goodies, this literary plasma, I'll put off opening it up . . . (*Looking up at her and again wistfully.*) I've gotten to be a greedy old man . . . I've learned to hoard my excitements—to ration them out . . .

JENNY (*gently*)
Why not?

He smiles at her. She smiles back. Looking past her, Mr. Barbirolli notices something in the hall. It amuses him.

BARBIROLLI
Miss Bishop, I think somebody's trying to get your attention.

Jenny turns around. Lonnie is standing in the hall, near the doorway. He's been trying to attract Jenny's attention, and looks ludicrous now—waving a bit, smiling at her, the goatee bobbing, the orderly outfit not quite fitting him. Jenny, of course, is embarrassed.

JENNY
What is it?

LONNIE (*Smiling, this is really his way of saying thank you for the job.*)
I just wanted to say hello . . .

BARBIROLLI
I've never seen *you* before . . .

LONNIE
No sir . . . My first day . . .

BARBIROLLI (*to Jenny, meaning this pleasantly*)
But I can see you know each other . . .

JENNY (*hating this*)
Yes . . .

BARBIROLLI
Well any friend of Miss Bishop is a friend of mine . . .

Lonnie is grinning, shrugging, while Mr. Barbirolli's radio starts erupting with static. He frowns, starts fussing with it. Lonnie comes closer to Jenny.

LONNIE (*whispers*)
That old o-fay, he's a sweet-talker, right, coz?

JENNY (*angrily*)
Do your work! (*Uncomfortable, because Mr. Barbirolli has looked up a little surprised by the harshness of her tone.*) It's no way to start a new job.

BARBIROLLI
You're absolutely right . . . (*To Lonnie, smiling*) One thing I know about Miss Bishop . . . She's always absolutely right . . .

LONNIE (*a little troubled by Jenny's attitude—trying to make things right*)
Mister, you're telling me, I've known her all my *life.*

JENNY (*her impatience showing*)
Don't stand here and *visit* . . . Go to work . . .

Lonnie nods. Clumsily, he tries to smile at her, to smile at Mr. Barbirolli. The goatee bobs. He goes off.

BARBIROLLI (*just to say something—already, he's looking at his package*)
 He seems like a good boy . . .

JENNY (*with a gesture of dismissal*)
 I don't know . . . I really haven't seen him for a long time . . . (*starting toward the door*) I'd better go to work myself . . . (*taking another step, looking back at him*) Happy reading . . .

BARBIROLLI
 Thanks to you . . .

Jenny smiles at him, goes out.

SCENE V (*Corridor*)

Carrie is working. She's not eavesedropping in the next scene, but she's trapped at her desk with work and can't help overhearing.

 Jenny comes out of Mr. Barbirolli's room. Lonnie has been loitering, waiting for her. He comes up to her.

LONNIE (*a half whisper*)
 Hey, Jen, what you get so hot about? I mean relax, big cousin. I ain't going to rock your boat.

Jenny looks into his earnest, unprepossessing face. She feels a certain futility in coping with him. She shrugs, keeps walking.

JENNY
 Just do your work, Lonnie . . . Don't socialize . . .

Lonnie nods. He moves after her.

LONNIE (*a whisper, earnest*)
I dig you, coz . . . I dig you . . . Anything else? . . .
Tell me—I want to know . . .

Jenny stops, turns, looks into his face—the goatee is pointed at her.

JENNY
Do you really want to know?

LONNIE
Sure I do, Jen. All you got to do is point me.

JENNY
The goatee, Lonnie . . .

LONNIE
Oh . . . (*A little chagrined, forcing a silly grin, touching the goatee.*) My fur? . . . You want me to part with my fur, coz?

Jenny has started to turn away, now she looks back at him.

JENNY (*a whisper, but very intense*)
Why are you such a fool? Why can't you have any pride? Button your jacket.

She wheels away from him. He's hurt, troubled. He stands there, holding his fingers on his goatee, his fur, and looking after her.

Jenny passes two cleaning women, Negroes, coming out of the kitchen area. They are also an unprepossessing type— they're laughing about something, making too much noise, clattering their pails too much as they come out. She looks at them—we see the contempt, the resentment she feels for them for their lack of pride. She stops.

JENNY
You're aware this is a hospital floor, aren't you?

71

The two cleaning women look into Jenny's face, feel her contempt. They dislike her for her attitude.

FIRST CLEANING WOMAN (*mimicking her*)

> We're *aware*, (*Saying the name sarcastically.*) Miss Bishop . . .

Jenny turns away from them, keeps walking. They look after her with dislike. In the foreground we have Carrie, looking on at the whole scene, troubled by it, but mostly for Jenny.

SCENE VI (*Medi-prep room*)

Jenny is there working on medications for the various patients. She is about to leave. Carrie comes in as Jenny prepares to wheel the cart out.

JENNY

> You can have the place all to yourself in just a few minutes.

CARRIE

> No, Jenny . . . Not yet . . .

Jenny sees Carrie's serious expression. She knows something is up. She stands there, waiting.

CARRIE

> We have a problem, Jenny . . . You have it, and I have it, too, because you're part of my responsibility.

CARRIE (*after a pause*)

> Jenny, there have been several complaints about you this past week . . .

JENNY (*startled*)

> About my work?

CARRIE

> Never your work, Jenny . . . Never in a million years your nursing . . . But it's all the rest, Jenny . . . Ever

72

since your cousin came to work here . . . I'm sorry
to go into this, but I guess it tensed you up about him
and about all the other Negro people working here . . .

JENNY

Oh . . .

CARRIE

You've gotten tough with some of the auxiliary personnel. Jenny, I'm afraid you've been putting pressure
on them . . . (*Saying this with great kindness.*) You're
yelling at them, riding them, and they're complaining.

JENNY (*wheeling now, bitter*)

They're complaining? . . . You don't know what they're
like . . . No self-respect, no sense of pride—or shame,
either . . . (*Shaking her head.*) You just don't understand them.

CARRIE

We weren't talking about me. But if you want me to
approach it from my point of view, I will. It comes
down to my having to run this floor.

JENNY

But if they don't do their work . . .

CARRIE

Then they'll hear from me. Jenny, you know how long
it took me to convince the office I'd make a better floor
nurse than instructor. I'm not about to let anyone prove
to them I was wrong. If you have complaints, come
to me. I'll decide what's efficient and what's not.

Jenny doesn't answer. Carrie continues with a smile.

CARRIE

Up to now I've had a fine team on the floor. All the
"gears" were well oiled and humming . . . It's not
going to be any other way . . . O.K.?

Jenny's mood changes now, too.

73

JENNY

All right, Miss Hayes . . . Thank you—I appreciate it.

Carrie nods. She looks at the tray Jenny has prepared. She smiles.

CARRIE

The first stop, Mr. Barbirolli, as usual?

JENNY (*smiling a bit*)

Well, there has to be a first . . .

Carrie nods. Jenny smiles at her—a strained smile, but a smile. She goes out.

SCENE VII (*Mr. Barbirolli's room*)

Jenny is going toward Mr. Barbirolli's room. Once again, despite the upset of the last meeting, she starts to feel better—she's always glad to see him. She enters the room. We don't see Mr. Barbirolli, we're on Jenny.

JENNY (*by habit*)

Okay—put down the book, come back to the twentieth century . . . (*Smiling, indicating the tray.*) It's *this* time again . . .

We see Jenny's face. We see her suddenly react. She goes to the door and calls—

JENNY

Miss Hayes!

She returns to the bed. We see what Jenny sees. Mr. Barbirolli is sick, desperately sick. He is hemorrhaging—a hemorrhage of the esophagus. He's delirious, moaning. Carrie enters the room.

CARRIE

Hemorrhage . . .

74

Carrie goes to Mr. Barbirolli. As she does, she kicks some-thing. It makes a splattering noise. Jenny looks down and sees a flat whiskey bottle, empty. Jenny picks it up, then looks at the moaning, ashen, drunken face of Mr. Barbirolli.

SCENE VIII (*Mr. Seligman's office*)

NARRATOR

A rumor starts that Lonnie is responsible for bringing the whiskey to Mr. Barbirolli who had been warned that drinking could kill him. When Jenny hears this rumor about her cousin, she confronts him.

Mr. Seligman is standing in a troubled way at the window, smoking. He turns around as Jenny enters abruptly through the already-open door of his office. Lonnie, who was seated, staring up defensively, frightened and sullen, also stands. His expression indicates that he senses, most of all, the ac-cusatory look on his cousin's face.

LONNIE

I didn't do it! . . . You hear?

JENNY (*a half whisper, but a sibilant one, a vicious one*)

I hear you, you trash, you . . . you animal . . . you Lenox Avenue Animal!

LONNIE

I came to see you!

JENNY

You're nothing . . . You came from nothing . . . All of you—you only know your dirty street games, your dirty street talk, your cheating, your lying, your dirt . . .

LONNIE

I ain't no dirt . . . I warn you, don't you treat me like

no dirt . . . and I ain't no jailbird . . . and I didn't sell no whiskey to that old man!

JENNY (*driving on, she's not about to listen to his denials*)
This is what I was afraid of, you hear? . . . In my heart, this is what I *knew* was going to happen. You were bound to drag me down, weren't you? . . . You and all the rest of you—that's what you do, all over, all over the place . . . You drag everything down . . . You won't be happy till we're all back there, back on those dirty streets . . . Back and dirty and dumb like you!

LONNIE (*shouting now himself*)
You shut your mouth, Jenny! I'm not studying to listen to your mouth right now! I didn't do it!

He starts to turn away from her. She grabs him.

JENNY
You did! . . . And you'll do something like it again, next time, wherever you sneak in next!

LONNIE
Shut up! . . . Shut your mouth!

JENNY
Wherever you foul up next, wherever you infect next—

LONNIE (*exploding now himself, grabbing her*)
I don't have to listen to you! I'm getting out of here!

More in desperation than in a desire to hurt her, Lonnie thrusts Jenny away from him. But he has strength, and she topples against the desk and falls to the floor. For a second, Lonnie stares at her, then he shakes his head against the injustice he feels, against this whole world, then he rushes out—past Mr. Seligman's futile outstretched arms, down the corridor, out, away.

76

Mr. Seligman turns to Jenny. She is getting up. He helps her.

SELIGMAN

Are you hurt, Miss Bishop? . . . Maybe you're hurt . . .

JENNY

No . . . (*Starting unsteadily toward the door.*)

SELIGMAN

I'm sorry . . . I'm so sorry, Miss Bishop.

Jenny turns to Mr. Seligman and she makes a gesture of helplessness.

JENNY (*a half whisper*)

Mr. Seligman, I've got to go back to Mr. Barbirolli— I've got to try and undo what that boy did . . .

Jenny turns, goes on out into the hallway.

SCENE IX (*Mr. Barbirolli's room*)

Jenny stands at the foot of the bed. Gail is looking down at Mr. Barbirolli who is starting to wake up. Carrie is in the doorway, she has gone back to other work, but is looking in right now.

NARRATOR

Although the patient has been near death for a period of time, he is now beginning to improve.

GAIL (*a whisper*)

Getting better!

Jenny however steps back. Carrie notices this.

JENNY (*to Carrie, a whisper*)

I don't want to face him now . . .

CARRIE (*a whisper*)
> *You* didn't do anything wrong . . .

Jenny nods. She knows this, but she stands there, on the periphery. Mr. Barbirolli is opening his eyes, looking up at the doctor, orienting himself.

GAIL (*speaking slowly, emphatically—this is the thing to do, reassure the patient*)
> Mr. Barbirolli? . . . Mr. Barbirolli—you are all right . . . You understand?

Mr. Barbirolli nods. But tears come to his eyes.

GAIL
> You have tubes in you, I know you're uncomfortable . . . but you're getting better . . .

BARBIROLLI (*with urgency*)
> Miss Bishop? . . . When will Miss Bishop be back?

GAIL (*seizing on this to calm him, to reassure him*)
> Why, she's right here, Mr. Barbirolli . . . She never left—(*Beckoning to Jenny.*)

Jenny reluctantly and slowly goes around until she is in Mr. Barbirolli's range of vision. She's bending down, on her knees, so that her face is close to his. She tries to go back to the old flipness in her manner with him.

JENNY
> Well, you're finally awake.

Mr. Barbirolli shakes his head. He has no time for games. And the tears come from his eyes.

BARBIROLLI
> I told you about it . . . That thirst, that dirty, disgusting thirst . . .

JENNY (*still trying to play the flip role*)
> And I might say, Mr. Barbirolli, your room is its usual mess . . . I'd say a little worse . . .

78

Mr. Barbirolli winces to himself. Jenny's forced smile turns his head away.

BARBIROLLI

I don't deserve your kindness . . . I never did . . .

JENNY

Too much talking, Mr. Barbirolli . . .

BARBIROLLI

You don't understand . . . I have to tell you about the bottle . . .

JENNY

I *know* about the bottle! Be calm . . .

BARBIROLLI (*turning to her*)

No . . . You didn't . . .

JENNY

I know! . . . Please—I know, be quiet . . . My cousin got you the bottle . . .

BARBIROLLI

What?

JENNY (*fighting tears, fighting her shame*)

Nobody blames you . . . We blame *him* for taking advantage of something you couldn't control . . . (*Fighting tears, shaking her head.*) So please, just be calm . . . There's nothing to say, please . . .

BARBIROLLI (*a horrified whisper—horrified at himself*)

It wasn't that way . . . God help me—Miss Bishop, it wasn't that boy who brought in the bottle! (*Shaking his head, crying, making himself say this.*) It was you . . . Not your fault, a trick, my fault, but *you* . . .

Jenny stares at him incredulously, and then not incredulously, because she sees the truth—the self-despising truth —on his face. Slowly she goes back toward him, looks down. He forces himself to look up at her.

BARBIROLLI

The last package from the book store . . . My friend's book store . . .

JENNY

Oh no . . .

BARBIROLLI

I got my friend to do it . . . He slipped it in the package . . . between Faulkner and Vladimir Nabakov.

JENNY

I . . . don't believe you.

BARBIROLLI

Why not? What would I lie for? To save the kid? (*Laughs derisively.*) Your cousin, huh? You don't like him, do you? Well, don't worry about it . . . You stay away from his kind.

Both Gail and Jenny are increasingly horrified.

BARBIROLLI

Stay away from them all, you hear me? You're different . . . got what it takes . . .

Carrie enters during the last words and steps to the bed.

CARRIE

Please, Mr. Barbirolli . . . don't talk about it now. The important thing now is to get well.

BARBIROLLI

Who told you that?

CARRIE

Now listen here. A lot of people worked darned hard to save you. So you just be grateful and do a little work yourself.

BARBIROLLI (*a whisper*)
They did?

CARRIE
They sure did.

Mr. Barbirolli closes his eyes.

BARBIROLLI (*half asleep already*)
Explain to her, Miss Bishop . . . what she just said . . .

In the background, Jenny just shakes her head. This is horrible for her.

BARBIROLLI
About saving me . . . Explain, Miss Bishop . . . Things I taught you while working out the idea of the books, and the bottle, and using you . . . (*Just getting the words out.*) Saving the unsavable . . . Impossible . . .

Mr. Barbirolli is asleep again. And in his sleep, he is crying. Jenny is staring down at him. And then a thought hits her. She trembles.

JENNY (*to Carrie*)
The boy . . . What I did to that boy!

SCENE X (*Corridor*)

Jenny already has reached the nurses' desk, has pulled open a phone book, is looking for a number.

JENNY (*as Carrie approaches*)
Maybe they don't even have a phone . . . (*With self-bitterness.*) I wouldn't know . . . I never called them . . .

CARRIE
Take it easy . . . There's lots of relatives *I* don't call either . . .

JENNY
It's different with me . . . (*Looking up, thinking about the word she has just used, facing it head-on now.*) Different . . .

CARRIE
    I don't think I like that word . . .

Jenny has found the number now. She starts to dial.

JENNY (*as she dials*)
    I hope he's there . . . Dear God, I hope he's not in
    some joint getting drunk, maybe getting in a fight or
    getting run over or something . . . (*Hearing the phone
    ringing, remembering, wincing.*) The things I said to
    him . . . The hateful things I said . . .

The ringing sound stops. The phone is being picked up.

MRS. HILL
    Hello . . .

*For just a second, Jenny is paralyzed, afraid to speak,
ashamed to speak. Then she does.*

JENNY
    Hello, Auntie—Auntie, this is Jenny . . .

*For reasons that should be clear in a second, Mrs. Hill isn't
too surprised to hear from Jenny right now—she's even
slightly pleased.*

MRS. HILL (*a little uncomfortably, but pleasantly*)
    Well, Sugar—I guess Lonnie Boy spoke to you then . . .

JENNY (*urgent*)
    Is here there, Auntie? . . . Isn't he there?

MRS. HILL
    No, Jenny, he ain't here, but he said for sure he was
    going to tell you I wanted you to come and eat with
    us on Sunday, like the old days . . . That scamp, that
    brainless scamp, didn't he say that?

The vision of the "old days" repels Jenny.

JENNY (*a half whisper*)

Auntie, he—he didn't tell me that . . . Please—where do you think he is right now?

MRS. HILL

I *told* you—I don't know . . . (*Getting to what to her is the big thing here, the mending of the fences.*)
Jenny, Jenny honey, I *do* want you to come . . . I was put out with you, I'll admit it, I was real put out with you for forgetting your own kin. But I do appreciate the way Lonnie's getting on, and I—

JENNY (*a half shout, breaking in*)

Auntie, something has happened, something rotten! . . . I made a mistake, an awful mistake, I made Lonnie feel bad!

Mrs. Hill immediately changes now, reverts to the suspicious attitude toward Jenny, which is the natural one.

MRS. HILL

What? . . . You tell me, you tell me right now—what did you do to that boy?

Carrie is watching Jenny compassionately.

JENNY (*into phone, a whisper, an ashamed whisper*)

Auntie, a man almost died here because he got hold of some whiskey . . . There were circumstances—I thought Lonnie did it . . . I—accused him . . .

Carrie can hear as Mrs. Hill shouts over the phone.

MRS. HILL

What's the matter with you? . . . Accusing your own, turning on your own, a boy like Lonnie, an uncertain boy—Where's your heart, you rotten girl? . . . And where is he—your cousin, who never done a wrong thing, never . . . Where is that boy now?

Jenny is trembling now. Carrie goes up, puts a comforting hand on her arm.

JENNY

Auntie, I don't *know* . . . I'm coming up there—I've got to *find* him!

MRS. HILL

Don't you come near here . . . You're my sister's girl, but I'm warning you—Stay away from me!

JENNY

I'm coming, Auntie . . .

MRS. HILL

Never mind about that. I ain't your Auntie no more.

JENNY

I'm coming up, Auntie . . . I've got to talk to Lonnie . . . I've got to find him and try to fix what I've done . . .

She hangs up the phone. Jenny stands up.

CARRIE

Would you like me to go with you?

JENNY

Up there, Miss Hayes? (*Shaking her head, saying the next words just as a simple fact.*) What do you know about up there?

She turns quickly, goes off. Carrie looks after her.

SCENE XI (*Staircase*)

Mrs. Hill lives on a Harlem residential street—converted brownstones, which are now tenements. A poor street but not a honkytonk street. A cab pulls up in front of one of the brownstones.

84

Jenny gets out and enters the building. Mrs. Hill is sweeping the stairs. Jenny enters the hallway, sees her aunt.

JENNY (*strained*)
He didn't come home, Auntie?

MRS. HILL (*her manner shows Lonnie hasn't*)
Just go on, leave us alone . . . Like you've been doing all these years.

JENNY
Please—tell me where to go look for him . . .

Mrs. Hill turns away, again looks up the street.

MRS. HILL
If I knew, don't you think I'd go look myself?

Jenny takes several steps up, then stops. Mrs. Hill doesn't look at her.

JENNY
Auntie—you have a right to know just what happened . . .

MRS. HILL (*not looking at her*)
I already figured *out* what happened from what you said on the telephone . . . (*Suddenly turning now, savagely grabbing Jenny with both hands, shaking her.*) From what you told me, you think it's so hard for me to figure out the rest, Miss Society Chick? . . . (*Still grabbing Jenny, trembling in her rage, her face close to Jenny's.*) And after you accused him, after you was so quick, so quick to point a finger, to look down, like you always were around here—after that, you opened that smart-talking mouth of yours, didn't you? (*Knowing this to be a fact, whispering these words.*) Words . . . Mean words, cruel words . . . You *cut* him with words, didn't you?

JENNY (*a whisper*)
> Yes . . . I'm sorry . . .

For a second, with their faces very close, Mrs. Hill stares at her. Then, as if sickened, she pushes Jenny away. Jenny goes down several steps, almost falls.

MRS. HILL
> Just get away from me . . . Just stay away . . .

JENNY
> No, Auntie! . . . I've got to talk to Lonnie . . .

MRS. HILL (*whirling around, looking at her again*)
> *Talk* to him . . . Why didn't you talk to him all this week? . . . He told me—in the hall, a quick nod, like the minister's wife and that's all . . . (*Leaning forward again, saying this slowly, intoning it.*) You was ashamed of him! Making him shave . . . How come you didn't throw soap at him, like some people do when you come to work at their house, like you never seen a bar of soap before?

There are footsteps beyond and behind Jenny. Contemptuous of Jenny, Mrs. Hill pushes her aside, looks. But it's not Lonnie—just another person coming in. Mrs. Hill steps aside, disappointed. The man walks up the stairs.

JENNY (*softly, almost begging*)
> Auntie—Auntie, I have pride—what's wrong with that?

Mrs. Hill doesn't want to answer. She just shakes her head restlessly.

JENNY
> The things I saw as a kid, the way people lived, the way they *had* to live . . . I knew there was something better in me, . . . I was scratching for that, Auntie— can't you understand that?

Again Mrs. Hill wheels on her.

MRS. HILL

Can't I understand that? . . . You big talking fool,
who do you think it was *gave* you them ideas in the first
place? . . . Who was it, you was maybe only nine, and
Lonnie was but five, took you to the public library
where there was a person picking books for children?
. . . Then to the church auditorium, when they had
them travelogues and talks and singing, too, by them
smart young folks from Howard University and that
Fisk University in Nashville? . . . Who was it, dressed
you, yes, and *washed* you, too, and with plenty of
soap, Miss, and took the two of you to I Am An American Day in Central Park, and all them places that
were for free, where a child could have its eyes opened
up wide?

JENNY (*startled, a whisper, remembering across the years*)
Oh . . . Oh, Auntie—I'd forgotten all that . . .

MRS. HILL
Who cares? . . . So along ago . . .

*She turns away from Jenny. But she does care, there's a rage
in her, a sense of outrage.*

MRS. HILL (*almost grudgingly, over her shoulder*)
All right—all right, it didn't take with Lonnie . . . It
didn't take with him, and he was mine, *really* mine,
and when he didn't show interest, maybe I put it all
aside, and you had to do it yourself . . . (*Turning
to her, fiercely.*) But don't sit there holding them clean
hands together and ask me if I can understand . . .

JENNY
Forgive me . . .

SCENE XII (*Mrs. Hill's living room*)

NARRATOR

When Lonnie comes back to the house, Jenny is still there, very eager to tell him how sorry she is for the way she treated him. Lonnie ignores her.

JENNY (*bending forward*)

Lonnie, please . . . give me a chance . . .

LONNIE (*to his mother*)

Ain't so many jobs going these days.

The process of being ignored now catches up with Jenny. Enraged, she throws herself at Lonnie, clawing at him, forcing him to acknowledge her existence.

JENNY

Listen to me!

Lonnie is lying back in his chair, Jenny sprawled half across him. Slowly, with great deliberation, he looks down at her upturned face, at her nailed fingers digging into his shoulders.

JENNY

You're going to listen to me! Listen! Listen! I have to tell you something!

LONNIE (*very quietly*)

You want to watch who you're touching there, woman. I'm a nigger.

Mrs. Hill is shocked.

MRS. HILL

Lonnie! . . .

Jenny recoils, her eyes wide with surprise. Then an eruption of hatred. Fed as it is by highly volatile guilt, it is hatred of remarkable intensity. She swings at the side of his head, hoping to hurt him, hoping indeed to kill him. The blow never lands. Lonnie catches her wrist. He looks at her an instant with contempt, then hurls her from him. Jenny slams against the wall, upsetting a table.

MRS. HILL

Lonnie! Stop that, you hear!

Lonnie comes out of the chair as though it is his intention to assault Jenny. Instead he crouches beside her, his face close to hers, his eyes blazing his contempt.

LONNIE

What have you got to tell me? About how sorry you are? About how you're sorry that I make you sick. Don't worry about it, Coz—you make me sick, too. You and your big ideas about making it with the man. Ain't nobody told you there ain't but one way to make it downtown? (*Sneers.*) And you're too black to pass.

MRS. HILL

Lonnie, you shut up! You shut your mouth!

Jenny shakes her head in horrified denial.

JENNY

No . . . No . . .

LONNIE

Yes, Coz . . . Yes. You're black.

He grabs her wrist, holds her hands up in front of her eyes.

LONNIE

Look at it! It's black! Black, Jenny!

Mrs. Hill is terribly agitated as she tries to pull Lonnie away from Jenny.

MRS. HILL

You come away . . . Come away, Lonnie. I don't like that kind of talk.

NARRATOR

The bitter controversy continues until Jenny convinces her cousin of her sincere wish to make amends for her mistake. She assures him of her deep desire to see him back on the job.

JENNY

Lonnie . . . I want to ask you something.

Lonnie looks at her sullenly, then nods.

JENNY

If you could go back . . . to the hospital . . . would you do it?

LONNIE

They ain't about to take me back there.

JENNY

But you didn't do anything. There's no reason why they shouldn't take you back.

LONNIE (*shrugs*)

Maybe.

JENNY

Would you go?

Lonnie isn't even sure he quite understands the question.

LONNIE

Sure I'd go. Why wouldn't I go?

JENNY

I . . . just wondered. (*Suddenly.*) Why, Lonnie? Why go back after what they did?

He looks pained, but decides to take pity on his foolish cousin and set her straight.

LONNIE

You're talking about how I ought to be proud or something. You want to know what I got to do? Whether it's your hospital or some place else?

JENNY

Yes. I want to know.

LONNIE

I got to get up in the morning and go downtown and work somewhere. That's all. It don't matter where I do it.

Jenny looks at Lonnie, a searching look and an admiring look. She nods.

SCENE XIII (*Hospital corridor*)

Side by side, Lonnie and Jenny enter the corridor. They are dressed in street clothes. They come to a turn in the corridor. Jenny takes Lonnie's hand and they start down the corridor.

STRIVERS

No Hero

by Jesse Stuart

When I could look over at the bright lights of Landsburg, I stopped to catch my breath and do some thinking.
For behind me lay the dark unfruitful hills where my crops
had failed. And in a shack among these hills, seven miles
away, I'd left Mollie with our three little ones. "Hester, we
have to have bread," was the last thing she'd said to me.
"We can't go another day without some kind of relief."
And when I started walking to Landsburg in the late afternoon, Mollie couldn't understand. I couldn't tell her what I
had in mind.

For nature had been against me. It wasn't that I wasn't
willing to work. I was willing to work. The drouth had
killed my crops. I couldn't make it rain. There just wasn't
anything I could do about it except see my garden truck,
corn, potatoes, and tobacco wilt in the hot June and July
sun. All I'd worked for was lost.

Nature was against me in another way that I couldn't
help. I'd grown up tall as a beanpole and slender as a
poplar sapling. In August I'd tried to get work with an
extra force, when the Railway Company was needing men.
The foreman took one look at me and said, "Not heavy
enough for your height. The lifting of crowbars, crossties,
and T-rails would break you in two." Then I tried to get a

96

job at the Auckland Iron Works, where they needed men. They gave me an examination and then put me on the scales. "Underweight," the doctor said. "We can't use you." It was that way every place I tried to get work.

Nature was against me more ways than one. And now I had to do some more thinking about Mollie and our three little ones before I tackled what I had in mind to do. Jim Harris told me about something in Landsburg. It was something they begged a man to do. It was hard to get a man to do it. But it was great fun for the people to see. Jim said the Landsburg Law had threatened to close the place up since one man, Hawk Weaver, was sent to the hospital.

In the distance below me I could see the bright lights along the streets and I could see one real bright spot in the town. This was the spot where I was going. For this was the fairground. I could hear the shouts of happy people coming from this spot and I could hear the music of the merry-go-round. "This way, this way," I could hear a man shout. "Three balls for the little dime, ten cents. Knock down three kitties and get yourself a quarter!" But this wasn't what I was going to do. It was harder than throwing balls at the kitties. It was something all the brave boys were afraid to do. And I wasn't brave either. I just needed the money. I had to have some money. And when I thought about it, my heart went up into my mouth.

But I'll be game, I thought. I'll try it. If they'll only let me try it after they see how tall I am and almost as light as the wind.

Then I started toward the brightest spot in Landsburg. My long beanpole legs soon covered the ground when I started walking. In a few minutes I'd reached the bright spot I'd looked over from the ridgetop. The Greenwood County people and the city people of Landsburg had filled the fairground. People were almost running over each other. They were standing in line to buy baseballs to throw at the kitties. They were standing in line to buy rings to throw over pegs where knives, alarm clocks, blankets, and pans were hanging. They were waiting to ride the merry-go-round and the merry-mixup. They were standing packed like sardines in front of a tent where two women danced and where a man beat a drum. And when the drummer and the dancers went into the tent and the announcer told them the "greatest show on earth would be inside the tent" they pushed each other down trying to get tickets before the tent was filled. Money was flowing like water and everybody was happy. I wished for a little of the money I saw coming from the fat pocketbooks. But my time was coming. Not now.

For Lefty Simmons, Landsburg's local boy, stepped upon the platform in boxing trunks and sparred with Slugger Stevens.

"Ladies and gentlemen, last evening Lefty Simmons and Slugger Stevens fought an even match," the announcer shouted through a megaphone, "and this evening they will fight to a finish. It's your local boy, Lefty, against the great and powerful Slugger Stevens! Ladies and gentlemen, right this way to see one of the greatest fights of all times!"

When Slugger and Lefty went inside the tent, the crowd rushed for tickets. I knew that my time would come next. It would come after this fight. For the people that loved to watch a fight would love to watch what I was going to try to do. Some of them might want to see a man killed. Though I wasn't sure about that. Yet, for years afterward they would talk about seeing Hester King's body mangled at the Landsburg Fair. But I didn't want to die. I'd thought this thing through and it was the only way I could see to make some quick money. I'd heard all my life, "Wherever there's a will, there's a way." I had the will. And I'd thought of the way.

There was one more night of the Landsburg Fair. And when I waited outside for the fight to be over, I heard screams and shouts of the people inside. "Kill 'im, Lefty, kill 'im!" I could hear men and women shout and scream. It must have been some fight, and a lot of people got worked up about it. For the Landsburg marshal and two deputies had to go inside the tent. But when the manager brought the fighters back onto the platform, he held up both their hands and said it was another draw and they would fight it out to a finish tomorrow night, the last night of the Landsburg Fair. They had fought to five draws, this made.

"Your local Lefty is some fighter," the announcer said. "He's stayed with the mighty Slugger for five nights!"

A great roar of applause went up from the people. For Lefty's face looked red and beaten and there was blood on his lips and nostils.

"Don't leave now, folks, don't leave," the announcer shouted through his megaphone. "Stand by for an important announcement!"

I knew what was coming now.

"We are looking for a man to stay with old Bruin five minutes tonight," the man shouted. "Is there a man in the crowd that will wrestle the greatest wrestler in the world! Is there a man that will take a chance wrestling this three-hundred-and-eighty-six-pound bear? If there is a man that will stay in the cage with him five minutes, he will receive twenty-five dollars! If a man will stay with him ten minutes, he will receive fifty dollars. He will receive twenty-five dollars for every five minutes he stays with old Bruin! That's a lot of money, folks! And if he wrestles Bruin," he shouted, "he will get an extra one hundred dollars."

"I'll try it, sir," I said, holding up my hand high above the crowd.

I looked around me and not another hand was up.

"That bear'll kill you, man," a big fellow said to me. "Hawk Weaver is in the hospital over a-tryin' to fight that bear! Ain't you afraid of 'im, Slim?"

"Yes, I am," I said.

"What are you a-gettin' in the cage with 'im for, then?" the man asked.

I didn't answer him. And I heard sighs go up all over the fairgrounds.

"Another victim," said a little man standing near me.

"Then come up here, Slim," the announcer said. "Let the crowd have a look at you!"

When I walked upon the platform, everybody laughed. The announcer looked me over and he laughed. Maybe he laughed at my big feet and long hands. But the whole crowd laughed, and they pushed up closer.

"How tall are you and how much do you weigh?" the announcer asked me.

"Six feet five and weigh one thirty-five," I said.

"Ever do any wrestling, Slim?" he asked me.

"Never did," I said.

"What do you do for a living?" he asked me.

"Right now I'm unemployed," I said.

Then the announcer asked me my full name and where I lived and I told him.

"This is Hester King from Buckrun Hollow back in Greenwood County," the announcer shouted to the crowd through his megaphone. "He's six feet five, weighs one thirty-five and he's never done any wrestling! And right now he's unemployed."

"He'll be employed when old Bruin gets a-hold of 'im," some man shouted from the crowd.

"Stomp old Bruin with your big number thirteens," another man laughed.

"Slap his face with your big fire-shovel hand," another man screamed.

Then everybody laughed. More people gathered in to have a look at me. It was the first time I'd ever faced a crowd like this. Everybody on the fairground was shoving closer.

"Nobody's stayed with that bear three minutes," said a big man that stood below me, resting his hand on the platform. "That's the catch. See, you don't get anything unless you stay five minutes! Hogg Morton stayed the longest. He stayed two minutes! Had the bear down once! But it like to 've kilt old Hogg before the referee could get 'im off! It's a mint of gold for this fair!"

"Buddie Walker didn't stay ten seconds," said a man standing beside the man that had spoken of Hogg Morton. "Bear just knocked him against the cage once and that was all there was to it."

"How long do you think you can stay with Bruin?" the announcer asked me.

"Five minutes," I said. "Maybe longer."

"Hester King says he can stay with Bruin five minutes, maybe longer," the announcer shouted gleefully.

"That's what Hester King thinks," a man shouted from the crowd. "That bear's a man-killer and shouldn't be allowed to wrestle civilized men at a street fair!"

"Then Mr. King says he'll stay with the bear five minutes or longer and you say he won't," the announcer said. "Let's see who is telling the truth! Maybe this tall man will surprise us!"

"Old Ichabod, the beanpole, will soon find out," somebody shouted from the crowd. "There won't be any draw in this wrestling match!"

"He wants to wrestle mighty bad," another man shouted. "Or he must need the money!"

"Wait until you see this man in wrestling trunks," the announcer said. "You'll see something. Worth the price of admission, folks!"

I followed the announcer from the platform down into the tent. The crowd surged up to buy tickets. When I went into a little dressing room and started taking off my clothes, I thought about Mollie, little Naomi, Sophie, and Hester, Jr.

101

Then I thought about going into the cage with the bear. I wondered just what would happen. And what if I can stay with 'im five minutes, I thought. Ten minutes! Fifteen, twenty, twenty-five minutes! One hundred and twenty-five dollars! What a fortune!

While I put my skinny legs into the big wrestler's trunks, I heard people pouring into the tent like honeybees into a hive. Only the people made more noise. It was a louder buzzing and there was so many jumbled words that I couldn't understand what anybody was saying. I could hear the word "kill" pretty often.

When I was ready, the manager told me the referee, Johnnie Norris, who owned the bear, would see that Bruin didn't hurt me, for he could handle him. He warned me not to be too scared and to stay with Bruin two minutes if I could.

"I must stay longer than that," I said. "I must stay five minutes!"

The manager laughed as he pushed back a flap of the tent and we walked into the arena beneath the big tent where the people were crowded close to the cage. The big black bear was inside the cage, walking around, looking between the iron bars at the people. He'd hold to the iron bars with his paws as he circled the cage and looked at the crowd.

"He'd like to get among us," said a well-dressed woman. "My, if I's a man, I wouldn't want to wrestle that ugly thing!"

When I walked among the crowd, everybody screamed with laughter.

"Ichabod Crane wrestling that heavy bear!" someone screamed.

People looked at my long skinny legs and wondered how they'd hold me up. They looked at my little waist measure.

"Not any bigger around the waist than the coupling pole in a jolt wagon," a big man said as I passed him.

"But look what feet and hands," another man said.

"Bear won't care for them," said a freckle-faced man with a bow tie that went up and down with his Adam's apple as he talked.

"Hate to see that poor man get what Hawk Weaver got," I heard someone say in a low voice. For I was near the cage door.

"Timekeepers here?" the announcer asked.

"Yep, we're here," said a tall man. "Kim Kiefer of Landsburg will help me keep the time!"

"All right, Al, you and Kim start your watches," Johnnie said, as he unlocked the cage door.

I thought of Mollie and my three little ones. That was the last thought I had before I stooped nearly double to go through the cage door.

"Shake hands with Bruin," Johnnie said. "He expects it. If you do, it will be easier for you!"

Bruin knew what his duties were. For he came up to meet me and Johnnie stepped aside when he reached me his paw. I shook his paw gently. And everybody in the tent became so quiet you could have almost heard a pin drop on the dirt-packed floor outside the cage. And my shaking Bruin's paw gently didn't help matters a bit. He backed away and then he came clumsily toward me with the full force of his three-hundred-odd pounds. He pushed me against the side of the cage with a wallop. He acted like he wanted to finish me in a hurry.

"Won't be long," said the freckle-faced man with the bow tie that worked up and down on his Adam's apple. He held his face close to the cage and peeped between the bars. But he was surprised when I got back to my feet and ran in between old Bruin's outstretched forepaws. That's the spot all the wrestlers didn't want to get. Old Bruin tried squeezing on me but I was too small for him to get the full power of his powerful arms. I hugged close to Bruin and put my hands gently on his back. Then he shoved me back and slapped at me again. He knocked me against the side of the cage. But it didn't hurt me and I didn't stay long. I ran back into his arms.

"Three minutes," said Kim Kiefer. "Longest anybody has stayed yet!"

The people surged closer. They packed around the cage.

"Down in front!" I heard them yell from the far sides of the arena. "Down in front!"

"Will he stay five minutes?" I heard wrestling fans asking each other.

I have to stay five minutes, I thought. And if I can just do. . . .

But old Bruin slapped me awfully hard and I hit the bars of the cage and saw stars.

"Four minutes," Kim Kiefer said.

"Three minutes and fifty seconds," said Al, the Street Fair's timekeeper.

"You're a little off," Kim Kiefer said. "My watch is right."

I was clinched with old Bruin again and I let my hands fall gently up and down his back like you'd rub a piece of silk on a washboard. Bruin wasn't as rambunctious with me as he had been. Johnnie Norris looked at us clinched there, and my chin down on old Bruin's head. We stood in the middle of the cage and the long lanky muscles of my bean-pole legs hooved higher than they ever had before. It looked like we were each trying to throw the other on the cage floor.

"Five minutes," Kiefer shouted.

"Seconds yet," Al said.

We stood there paw-locked and arm-locked and time was fleeting. Once Johnnie Norris passed around us and he had a worried look on his face. But I watched the referee to see that he didn't prod the bear to make him try to finish me. Spectators were watching through the bars. Women were sitting upon men's shoulders so they could see into the cage. They were watching Johnnie Norris too. Hundreds of eyes were trained on him as he moved around through the cage with a mysterious air and a worried look on his face.

"Nine minutes," Kim Kiefer shouted.

Al didn't say anything.

One minute more, I thought. Just one minute more.

Then Bruin started pushing me. And I braced my feet away out from him for I was tall and I leaned like a prop. Yet, I had my chin on his head.

"Ten minutes," Kiefer said.

"Lacks ten seconds of being ten minutes," Al grunted.

Then Bruin put his red tongue out like a tired dog. I felt his hot breath sizzle past my ear. The sweat was pouring from my face and running in little streams down my body. Holding a bear up as big as Bruin wasn't an easy task.

"Has he hypnotized that bear?" someone shouted.

And just about that time, Bruin pushed me to the floor. But he didn't come down on me. I stayed down to rest a minute. He panted harder and everybody could see his long red tongue and his full set of pretty white teeth. He stood in the middle of the cage like a very tired wrestler.

"Fourteen minutes," Kim Kiefer said.

Then there were shouts that went up from the people.

"He might even wrestle old Bruin yet," the fellow said who was wearing the bow tie. He said the words so fast the bow tie jumped up and down his neck with his Adam's apple like a tree frog.

I came back to my feet and Bruin came to meet me, slapping gently with his paws. I did a little footwork around the cage until his front paws were spread apart and then I rushed in and clinched Bruin.

"Fifteen minutes," Kiefer said.

Seventy-five dollars, I thought. Give me five minutes more.

And when I put my chin back on Bruin's head and braced my feet with my big hands planted on Bruin's back, this time Bruin went down and I went down beside him. Johnnie Norris ran up to look at our shoulders. Al ran up and looked between the bars. And the crowd screamed loud enough to raise the tent.

Bruin's weight on my left arm hurt a little. But my right arm was around his neck. My chin was still on top of his head. And we lay there, stomach to stomach, side by side, in wrestling embrace.

"What's wrong here?" Johnnie Norris said to the Fair's timekeeper. "Al, you go get the boss!"

"But who will keep time with Kiefer?" Al asked.

"I will," Johnnie said, as Al started pushing his way through the crowd.

"Referee can't serve in two capacities at one time," a big man with a handlebar mustache said as he put his face against the cage bars.

Shouts went up again from the people.

"Nineteen minutes," Kiefer said.

"Ten seconds till," Johnnie Norris said.

"Who said old Ichabod Crane couldn't wrestle," said the man with the Adam's apple. "He'll ride that bear yet!"

They didn't know it, but I knew Bruin was ready for a rest on the floor even if we were in a wrestlers' clinch.

When the boss, Solway Meadows, came running into the tent, his face looked as sour as if he'd bitten a green persimmon when he looked inside the cage and saw us lying side by side.

"Twenty minutes," Kiefer shouted.

"What's wrong, Johnnie?" Solway Meadows asked.

"Old Bruin just can't ride 'im," Johnnie said.

"Now you're a-talkin'," somebody shouted. "Old Ichabod Crane will ride that bear yet! He's some wrestler!"

"Old Bruin didn't find Hawk Weaver when he got hold of old Ichabod," said the big sports fan with the handlebar mustache. He tried to stick his face between the cage bars, and he worked his mustache like a rabbit works its whiskers.

"Twenty-four minutes," Kim Kiefer shouted.

"Old Ichabod said he'd stay with old Bruin five minutes and maybe longer," the big sports fan shouted and wiggled his handlebar mustache. "He's a-doin' more than he said he would!"

"Twenty-five minutes," Kiefer shouted.

Then the bear rolled over on his back.

The loudest scream of all went up from the crowd. There were screams, shouts, and whistles.

"Look at the shoulders there, referee," the old sports fan shouted. "Let's have the count. Bruin's down! He's down!"

Bruin didn't offer to get up. His big mouth was open and you could count the white teeth in his mouth and take a look at his pretty red tongue.

"You must have played my bear foul," Johnnie Norris said.

"I did not," I panted. "You'll see Bruin's not hurt. He's tired but happy!"

"First time that bear was ever ridden," Solway Meadows said.

"First time anybody ever stayed with 'im over two minutes," Al said.

But from the screams of the people it was hard to hear another word. When Johnnie Norris got Bruin up from my arm, he found out whether he was hurt or not. Bruin gave him a lick on top the head that sent Johnnie reeling toward the other side of the cage where he staggered a few times, shook his head, and seemed to do a little dance on wobbly legs as he slumped down to the floor.

"What do you know about that?" Al said.

"You see I didn't hurt old Bruin," I said to Solway Meadows. "He's a hard bear to handle!"

"Two hundred and twenty-five dollars!" said the freckled-faced man wearing the bow tie. "Think of it! Ichabod Crane rode old Bruin!"

Solway Meadows let me through the cage door, while Al

dragged Johnnie outside where he'd have a more comfortable sleep.

"Same thing old Bruin done to Hawk Weaver," a tall beardy-faced fan said as the old sports fan with the big mustache and the young man with the bow tie and as many others as could gather around me lifted me upon their shoulders. They carried me out of the tent and over the Landsburg fairgrounds, shouting "Here's Ichabod Crane! He rode the bear!"

And everybody laughed and screamed and shouted. They waved their hands at me and the women and girls threw handkerchiefs toward me. I was a hero for that night. But they didn't know how I did it. They paid me the money but told me the bear wouldn't wrestle on Saturday night. I didn't tell them or anybody what a friend I'd made of Bruin. I didn't tell them I had once owned a pet bear in the upper Peninsula of Michigan when I was trying to cut cord wood, and that I knew a bear liked to be rubbed between the ears and on the tummy. I suppose it wasn't exactly fair, but Mollie and the kids had to eat. Gentling old Bruin was an easy dollar.

MORE STRIVERS

NELLIE BLY
by Nina Brown Baker

No Girls Wanted

Nellie's brothers did not object to the New York venture. If their young sister must go on with her newspaper career, it was better that she do it in a distant city.

Her mother's only worry was to make sure that she found a good home. It must be a place with regular meals, and someone to see that she wore her rubbers on rainy days.

A friend recommended a New York boardinghouse kept by a respectable widow. The landlady was said to be a kindly soul who looked after her guests like a mother, and who "set a good table" besides. It sounded exactly right for Nellie. She wrote and reserved a room.

Traveling alone for the first time in her life, she took the train to Jersey City, where the railroad ended. There she changed to a ferry boat to take her across the Hudson River to Manhattan Island.

The train had been hot and dusty, but she found the short ferry trip enchanting. The towers of Manhattan seemed to float above the blue water, their windows turned to blazing gold by the rays of the setting sun. Tall ships in the harbor fringed the shore, stretching up and down the river. Nellie's heart beat fast as the boat slid into the ferry slip, gateway to this magic city.

The motherly landlady had come to meet her. She led the way to the horse-drawn bus which took them to her house on upper Lexington Avenue.

It was a tall brownstone in a row of similar houses. The landlady explained that it had been the family home before her husband's death. Like so many widows of her day, she now supported herself by opening her home to paying guests.

Nellie was impressed by the handsome front parlor and the graceful stairway. The splendor faded quickly as she mounted the stairs. Her own room proved to be a tiny attic chamber, once a servant's room. It was simply furnished and stiflingly hot. But it was clean and cheap, and the landlady seemed kind. Nellie asked nothing more.

As soon as she was left alone, she drew out the list she and Mr. Madden had made. It contained the names and addresses of every newspaper in New York. Most of them were on Park Row, near the City Hall. "If the first one turns me down," she reflected, "I can try the next without spending more carfare. That's something, anyway."

Mr. Madden had warned her that she must expect to be turned down. "They just might give you a chance on the woman's page, writing about fashions and recipes. Oh, I know that isn't what you want, Nellie. You want to do real reporting. Well, not a paper in New York employs a woman to do the sort of thing you've been doing for us. If there's a place for you on a New York paper, you'll have to make it for yourself."

"I'll make it," she had told him confidently.

Her confidence was still high as she went over the list now. The *Sun*, the *Tribune*, the *Times*, the *Herald*, the *Post*, the *World*—oh, there were so many of them! All these editors couldn't be prejudiced against girl reporters. And even if they were, they couldn't be any more prejudiced than Mr. Madden had been at first. He'd talked about having to make a place for herself here. Well, she'd had to do that on the *Dispatch*, too. And she'd done it. She could do it again. She *would* do it again.

She smoothed her hair and went down to supper. Her fellow guests, four or five middle-aged school-teachers, were pleasant but distant. The conversation was all of school affairs, of which she knew nothing. As soon as the meal was over she escaped to her room. She unpacked quickly and was in bed by the time darkness fell. Tomorrow would be a long day.

It was shorter than she had expected. Following her landlady's directions she took a horsecar down to Park Row. By early afternoon she had visited every office on her list.

Not once did she get beyond the office boy. Some of them were civil, and some were curt. Each demanded to know what she wanted to see the editor about. When she admitted she was looking for a job, they told her flatly that the paper never hired women reporters.

As Mr. Madden had predicted, his letters of introduction did no good. She was invited to leave them, with her address. The editors would write if they wanted to see her. No, it was no use asking them to see her now. That was what office boys were for; to keep their bosses from being pestered by unwelcome visitors.

She was more puzzled than discouraged as she left the last office. "Where did I go wrong?" she asked herself. She found a bench in City Hall Park and sat down to think it out.

"I can't say I've been refused a job," she told herself. "I haven't asked for one yet. Those boys couldn't hire me if they wanted to. It's the editor who does that. And I haven't seen a single editor. Now that's what I have to work out. How do I get into an editor's office?"

From where she sat, she could see the front doors of

several newspaper offices. A trickle of men passed in and out. Any one of them might be the editor who could decide her whole future. What if she went up to him there on the steps? Grabbed his arm? Made him listen?

She shook her head. If she tried anything like that, the man could have her arrested for disturbing the peace. And very likely he wouldn't be an editor, anyhow. She mustn't waste her time in wild fancies. This problem called for some real thinking.

Sitting there in the shade, she thought long and hard. How had she got her job on the *Dispatch*? Not by going to the office and asking for it. She had attracted Mr. Madden's attention by writing him a letter. It was a silly letter. Just the same, it had brought her an invitation to visit the editor. And the visit had resulted in the job.

She sat up straight, her weariness forgotten. A letter to the editor—that was it. A very different sort of letter this time, though. Sensible and businesslike, telling of the work she had done in Pittsburgh. She had brought a scrapbook with her, containing all her published articles. She'd copy the best ones and enclose them in each letter.

Nellie was never without pencil and paper. She took out a pad now and began drafting her letter. All afternoon she sat on, deaf and blind to her surroundings. The homeward rush was beginning when at last she put the scribbled pad back into her handbag. Swaying from a strap in the crowded car, her mind went on forming words and phrases.

"I won't be wanting supper," she told her landlady on the way up to her room. For half the night she worked on, carefully copying the articles from her scrapbook. It was past midnight when she finished, too late to buy stamps for her half-dozen letters. She went to bed hungry and exhausted but supremely hopeful.

The letters went out next morning. She figured that she could not expect an answer for at least three days. Those three days she devoted to exploring New York.

There were wondrous sights to see. The Statue of Liberty, not yet one year old. The Brooklyn Bridge, one of the seven wonders of the modern world. The glittering department stores, the magnificent churches, the quaint foreignness of the immigrant neighborhoods. Nellie saw it all, by bus and streetcar, and on her own tireless little feet. She must hurry, she told herself, to learn her way around the city. It would help when she got her job.

She need not have hurried. The fourth day brought no job. Nor did the fourth week. A few editors wrote politely that they had no openings but would place her application on file. Most of them did not trouble to write at all.

Again Nellie had to ask herself, "Where did I go wrong?" Her letter and samples of her work were accomplishing nothing. This, then, was not the way to go about it. She must find another way.

She went back to her experience with Mr. Madden. She had first attracted his attention by criticizing an article in his paper. Suppose she tried that here?

She tried it. Every day she bought all the leading papers. She combed the editorial pages for an article to suit her purpose. When she found one, she sat down and wrote a reply. Sometimes she praised the article but added some reflections of her own. Sometimes she disagreed and gave her reasons for it. Neither plan worked. So far as any response was concerned, she might as well have dropped her letters into the East River.

The hot, steamy New York summer dragged on. Nellie had a spurt of hope when she read in the New York *World* of a proposed balloon ascension in St. Louis. The *World*'s owner, Mr. Joseph Pulitzer, also owned a St. Louis paper. He was sponsoring a bigger and better balloon, which would carry its passenger higher into the sky than man had ever gone.

Why should the passenger be a man? It occurred to Nellie that a girl passenger would be far more sensational. Men had gone up in balloons before. She could not remember that a woman ever had.

She dashed off a series of letters to Mr. Pulitzer, urging him to let her make the ascent. No answer came.

She began again to make the rounds of the newspaper offices. This time, instead of asking for a job, she came in with outlines of stories she would like to write. They were along the lines that had brought her success in Pittsburgh. The crowded firetrap tenements of the East Side, the lack of drinking fountains for work horses, the wretched plight of homeless children—there was no lack of material. If only she could make the editors see it!

Once in a great while she managed to talk her way past the office boy, to some harassed editorial assistant. "You can leave your outline," he would tell her grudgingly. "We'll let you know if we can use it." How she came to hate those well-worn words! They meant nothing but a polite dismissal.

Her worst day came toward the end of August. Up to now, she had had no money worries. The fund she brought with her was enough to pay her board, although it was melting fast. Carfares and newspapers were expenses she could not avoid. But there were still ten comforting ten-dollar bills in the little purse she carried in her skirt pocket. Money was safer there than in her beaded handbag, she thought. A bag might be snatched from her, but no one could even suspect the hidden pocket in the skirt's wide folds.

She took the horse car down to City Hall, and settled herself on her favorite bench in the little park. By this time, she knew all the editors by sight; when they arrived, and when they left their offices.

Today she was determined to make another attempt upon the *World*. The time for the balloon ascension was drawing near. If she were to persuade Mr. Pulitzer to let her be the passenger, she must do it quickly.

"I'll talk to him today or die in the attempt," she vowed,

and settled down to wait. It would be an hour at least before the great man appeared at his office. She had watched often enough to know his usual time. It would be a tiring wait, but it was cooler here under the trees than in her airless little attic room.

"Lemonade, Miss?"

She looked up as a boy approached the bench. He was carrying an open pail of lemonade and a battered tin cup. Nellie did not usually buy from these street vendors. But the boy looked fairly clean, and ice tinkled invitingly in the pail.

"Ice-cold," he urged, seeing her hesitation. "I just brung it from home, Miss. Ain't nobody drunk out of the cup yet, if you're fussy."

"I'm pretty fussy," she admitted. Then she smiled down into the anxious young face. "All right. I guess it won't hurt me for once. You can pour me a cup, sonny."

She reached into the pocket for her purse. Her groping fingers failed to find it. She twisted on the bench, pulling the full skirt around. With both hands she held the pocket open. It was empty.

"I'm sorry," she told the boy. "I—I've lost my money."

With a scowl he poured the drink back into his pail and scurried off. She did not see him go.

"How could it have happened?" she was asking herself. "Did I leave it on my dresser? No, because I had it when I paid my carfare. Maybe I put it into my bag."

She turned out the little bag without hope. There was nothing there but her handkerchief and pencil and paper.

She thought back to her trip downtown. She had sat next to a fat woman with a bundle of washing on her lap. The woman had squirmed and shifted a good deal, but Nellie had supposed that was because the bundle was awkward. She must have seen Nellie pay her fare when the conductor came through. She would have seen her put the purse back into her pocket. Had the woman sat on the pocket side? Yes, she had. Those fat fingers constantly fiddling with the bundle must have crept into the hidden pocket.

That was how it happened. And now what? The hundred dollars was to have seen her through another two months. It was gone. She was left without even carfare to take her back to her boardinghouse. She would have to walk home. And borrow a stamp from her landlady to write to Mama.

Mama would send her some money, of course. But she was living with Albert this summer. It would not be possible to draw the money and send it without Albert's knowing. He couldn't stop Mama, of course. It was her money. But how he would gloat!

She wished now she hadn't written such cheerful letters. Things were a little slow in summer, she had said, but she had good prospects. Any day now she expected to have wonderful news of her new job.

"Well, this is the day," she told herself grimly. "I said I'd see Mr. Pulitzer today. Now I've *got* to see him. And he's *got* to give me a job!"

She could scarcely bear the waiting now. It seemed ages before her straining eyes caught sight of the Pulitzer horses. The carriage clattered across the cobblestones and drew up with a flourish before the *World* Building.

The coachman leaped down and opened the carriage door. Resplendent in frock coat and silk hat, his gold-headed cane gleaming in the sunlight, Joseph Pulitzer strolled leisurely up the low steps. A bowing doorman ushered him inside.

"I'll give him twenty minutes to get settled," Nellie decided. Her pretty face was pale, and her little fists were clenched with determination. "Then I'm going in there. And I'm not coming out until he's hired me."

The Great Mr. Pulitzer

But you can't sit here, Miss. You're in everybody's way!"
The boy sounded a little desperate.

Nellie smiled at him.

"I'll be glad to move into Mr. Pulitzer's office. But I'm
going to sit right here until I see him. I told you that."

"Yes, and I told you you can't see him! I've told you and
told you, Miss. *Nobody* sees Mr. Pulitzer, unless he sends
for them. I don't dare go in there myself except when he
rings for me. You'll just get me into trouble if you keep
on sitting there."

"I'd hate to make trouble for you," Nellie said sweetly.
"When I see Mr. Pulitzer, I'll tell him it wasn't your fault."

"But—oh, what's the use? Sit there, then. Keep on sitting
till you get sick of it. But you'll never get near the boss."

He turned away in disgust. Nellie settled herself more
firmly in her chair. At least she had penetrated to the
World's city room, which she had never managed before.

It had been easy. She had just come upstairs and walked
quietly through the open door as though she belonged there.
No one but the office boy had paid her the slightest attention.

All about her was the bedlam of a newspaper going to
press. Reporters were dashing in and out. Subeditors worked
away at their desks. Once in awhile one of them got up to
shout into a curious black box on the wall. Nellie had heard
about a new invention called the telephone, but this was
the first time she had seen one. The telegraph instrument
clicking away in the corner was familiar from her *Dispatch*
days. The *World* must be a very up-to-date paper, to have
telegraph and telephone both.

If she had not been so worried, she could have enjoyed
watching the city room sights. As it was, she could not
get her mind off her troubles. If she left here without a

job . . . ! But she wouldn't. She would sit right here until she got one.

The minutes dragged by, and still she sat, quietly waiting. On the far side of the room were two private office doors. One was closed. The other stood open, showing an untidy desk and empty chairs. She guessed that Mr. Pulitzer must be behind the closed door. Would it ever open for her? Oh, it must, it must!

Excuse me, ma'am. A big man, coming in from outside, had nearly tripped over her feet. He caught the back of her chair to steady himself and looked at her in surprise. Then he frowned.

"Visitors are not allowed in the city room, young lady," he said curtly. "If you're a friend of one of the reporters, you'll have to wait for him downstairs."

The office boy hurried over to them.

"She's nobody's friend, Mr. Cockerill! She's just—well, she acts like a crazy woman to me. She's been sitting there all morning, and I can't make her budge. Will I call a cop and have him throw her out, sir?"

"Not yet." The big man turned to Nellie.

"I am John A. Cockerill, managing editor of this paper. If you have business here, tell me what it is. If not, I must ask you to go quietly before we call the police."

Nellie took a deep breath.

"I'm sorry to be a nuisance, Mr. Cockerill. But I came to see Mr. Pulitzer. I'm going to stay here until I do."

Her voice was soft but very firm. The editor looked puzzled. Then he gestured toward the empty office.

"Come in here," he said shortly.

Nellie hesitated. Then she got up and followed him. A quick glance showed her an inner door connecting with the other private office. Joseph Pulitzer, she knew, was behind that closed door.

Mr. Cockerill offered her a chair and sat down behind his desk.

"Now, young lady. You may take my word for it that you won't see Mr. Pulitzer unless I say so. I can give you five minutes to convince me. To begin with, who are you?"

"My name is Nellie Bly," she began eagerly. "And I want—"

"Nellie Bly? I've seen your letters. You're the young woman who wants to go up in the St. Louis balloon. Mr. Pulitzer has already made up his mind about that. The answer is no. And it's final. No amount of coaxing ever changes *his* mind. Now don't let's have any tears," he added hastily. "That's one reason women don't belong in business. They always burst out sobbing when things don't go to suit them."

There were tears in Nellie's eyes, but she blinked them back.

"I'm not going to cry, Mr. Cockerill. If you're sure Mr. Pulitzer won't change his mind—yes, I can see you *are* sure. All right. I won't bother him about the balloon. But I still want to talk to him. About something entirely different."

"You don't give up easily, do you?" There was unwilling admiration in his voice. "I know more about you than you might think, Miss Nellie Bly. You've written a number of letters to Mr. Pulitzer. They were all passed on to me. I take it you're in earnest about wanting a job on the *World.*"

"Oh, I am, Mr. Cockerill!" Nellie's voice shook with eagerness. "Going up in the balloon was just one of my ideas. I have lots of others. New York is full of good stories that never get into the papers. All sorts of dreadful things are going on that need to be exposed. I'd like to do here what I did in Pittsburgh. Out there I—"

"Yes, you wrote us about your work on the *Dispatch*," he cut in.

Nellie flushed. It was plain that time was more precious here than in easygoing Pittsburgh. Cockerill saw her embarrassment and went on more kindly, "I'm a busy man, Miss Bly. So is Mr. Pulitzer. But I like your grit. I think you've earned your interview. I warn you, though, you must make it brief. Wait here."

He went to the inner door, knocked, and entered, closing the door behind him.

And now, for the first time, real panic swept over Nellie. The balloon plan was hopeless, she could see that. What else was there? What other idea could she offer that would get her a job?

She had told Mr. Cockerill that she had lots of them. But what did she have that was big enough, different enough, to offer Mr. Pulitzer? Her whirling brain could not produce one. If only she had time to think, to pick and choose!

But she had no time at all. In only a minute or two, the inner door opened. Mr. Cockerill beckoned to her.

The great Mr. Pulitzer sat behind his huge mahogany desk, frowning a little through his thick-lensed glasses. Although it was a well-kept secret at that time, his sight was failing fast. But except for his red-rimmed, bloodshot eyes, he was an extremely handsome man. He was tall and bearded, with an almost kinglike dignity. Hardier souls than Nellie's had quaked in that imperial presence.

He did not rise as Cockerill introduced her.

"Sit down, young woman," he ordered. "I hear you've taken a good deal of trouble to see me. Now let's hear what you want to see me about."

"Yes, sir." Nellie gulped. "I—I want to be a reporter on the *World*, Mr. Pulitzer. I've already had newspaper experience in Pittsburgh, and—"

He silenced her with an impatient gesture.

"We're not interested in your past. Cockerill says you claim to have some original story ideas. I doubt it. We have good men on the *World*, and they cover the city pretty thoroughly. But if you know something that hasn't been done, and that's any good, I'll listen. Make it brief."

Nellie's hands twisted desperately in her lap. Her mind was a complete blank. "She acts like a crazy woman to me," the office boy had said. If she didn't speak up now, Mr. Pulitzer would think the same thing.

Suddenly, out of nowhere, a great light came flooding in. She spoke without stopping to think.

"I want," she said deliberately, "to act like a crazy woman."

She paused, actually enjoying the amazement in the men's faces. This had been one of her most cherished story ideas. She had sent the *World* an outline of it weeks ago. They had paid no attention to it. Probably no one had even read it. She had almost forgotten it herself. But now it came back to her, complete in every detail.

"It would be sensational," she went on eagerly. "I'd get myself committed to the city asylum for the insane poor. I'd find out what really goes on behind those barred windows. Who knows how those poor people are treated? They can't complain, whatever is done to them. The authorities would just say, 'Oh, they're crazy, they're raving.' A lunatic is completely helpless. He has to eat what he's given, and do what he's told. The city spends a lot of money to keep up the asylum on Blackwell's Island. How do the taxpayers know what they're getting for their money? There are stories around town about waste and mismanagement over there. You must have heard them yourself, Mr. Pulitzer."

"Oh, stories," he said. "Of course I've heard stories. I once sent a reporter to the Island to look into them. But he didn't find anything amiss."

"Of course he didn't," she said scornfully. "Everything would be all tidied up for him. He'd see what he was meant to see and no more. But I wouldn't go as a reporter. I'd be a patient. I'd see it from the inside. And I'd stay long enough to find out just what conditions are. Then I'd write it up for the *World*. Don't you think your readers would be interested in such a story?"

She held her breath as the two men exchanged glances. Cockerill looked eager, but Mr. Pulitzer shook his head.

"It wouldn't do, Miss Bly. You are not insane. Patients are examined by a doctor before they are sent to the Island. You would never pass their examination. And even if you did—well, let me speak frankly. You seem to be a young lady of refinement. You could not endure life in the insane wards, if it is as bad as you think."

"For a good story, I can endure *anything*," Nellie said sturdily. "And I can fool the doctors. I know I can. I'll do it all on my own, Mr. Pulitzer. The *World* won't be connected with the scheme if it fails. All I'd want you to do would be to get me out after I'd had a week there. A week should be long enough."

"Getting you out mightn't be so easy, once you've been committed," Mr. Cockerill warned.

Nellie looked dismayed. But Mr. Pulitzer said easily, "There'd be no trouble about that. All it takes is for some respectable citizen to come forward and offer to give her private care. Our lawyer could do it. Once she was free and writing her stories, of course, it would all come out. I suspect there'd be some red faces around City Hall."

"Then you'll let me do it, Mr. Pulitzer?"

"You'd have to be honest," he said thoughtfully. "Things may be better over there than we think. The *World* doesn't deal in made-up horrors. We'd want whatever good things you find, as well as the bad."

"I understand that," she said eagerly. "I'll put down exactly what I see, Mr. Pulitzer, good or bad. All I care about is to find the truth, and tell it. I always do."

Mr. Pulitzer glanced at his watch.

"Well, you've given us something to think about, Miss Bly. I may say frankly that it's the most original idea we've come across in some time. We'll talk it over and let you know."

In bitter disappointment Nellie followed Cockerill back to his office.

"And I thought he was going to say yes," she mourned.

"He is." The editor laughed. "But he doesn't like to be hurried. Don't worry, Miss Bly. You're as good as on the *World* payroll right now."

A delighted smile chased away the gloom. After the dreaded presence of Pulitzer, this big, bearlike editor seemed an old friend. Impulsively she gave him her confidence.

"If I'm on the payroll, Mr. Cockerill, could I collect a little pay in advance? You see, I had my pocket picked, coming down here. I haven't a penny to get home."

"I'll give you a twenty-five-dollar order on the cashier— cash it as you go out," he said absently. "But don't go yet, Miss Bly. We'd better work out the details of this scheme of yours. When the big boss gives the word to go ahead, he'll expect action right away. Sit down here and tell me just exactly how you plan to turn yourself into a lunatic."

ONE MAN'S NAME

by Harry Golden

Levi Strauss was born in Bavaria, Germany, in 1829. In time, he became clerk of registry for the village of Bad Ocheim. It was the same job his father and grandfather had held before him. Perhaps this was because Levi's family was Jewish, and Jews were not allowed to own land or do much else in Bavaria.

Not only was Levi denied real opportunity to get ahead, but he was also very lonely. His parents were dead, and his brothers Willi and Jacob had gone to America. People in Germany said that in the new land gold could be picked up in the streets. Levi imagined his two brothers dressed like rich men, wearing beaver coats and shiny boots. Finally, unhappy and more lonely than ever, Levi sold his home and bought a boat ticket to New York.

Everyone from steerage was on deck as closer and closer the ship sailed toward the harbor of New York. Already the city had a skyline and they could make out the buildings standing in the sun, glinting, beckoning. The fears that beset strangers in a strange land left them, for they saw not only a brand-new city before them but a brand-new idea. Levi talked to the people he had traveled with and all were as excited as he. Together they sat on the deck at night, humming the familiar songs from the old country, exchanging past histories, and pledging friendship in the new land. Now they were almost there, and few realized they had taken a part, albeit a small part, in one of the great adventures of all history.

Willi and Jacob had waited all day, first outside the picket fence on the dock and later in the visiting room of Castle Garden. When they ran toward each other Levi Strauss knew he had come home. They clasped and kissed, and Levi told them Johann had indeed married Maria and Otto had come home to go to work in his father's cobbler shop and the winters had been as cold as ever since they left.

Then Levi remembered the gold in the streets and the beaver coats and the polished boots, none of which did Willi and Jacob seem to possess.

"There is no gold in the streets," said Willi.

"In fact," said Jacob, "many Germans who came here are building the streets."

"Which is why we don't wear polished boots; the streets are muddy eight months of the year," said Willi.

"And cloth coats keep us warm enough, especially with a wool scarf," finished Jacob.

"But how, then," asked Levi, confused, "how do we eat?"

"We work!" shouted Willi.

"There is work here," said Jacob. "More than enough work for all of Germany, for all of Europe."

"And what work do we do?" asked Levi.

"We are peddlers," said Willi.

"Gypsies?" asked Levi.

"Gypsies, if you will," said Jacob.

"In Bad Ocheim," said Levi, "the Strausses were always clerks of registry."

"But we are not in Bad Ocheim," said Jacob. "We are in the New World. A man here is what he makes himself."

Willi and Jacob spent the next two weeks teaching Levi to speak some English and to use American money. They also taught him how to buy merchandise at the warehouse, how to fix his peddler's bundle, and how to sell his wares to his customers.

By the third week, Levi himself was ready. He made his own selections at the warehouse and fixed his own pack. He traveled around the outskirts of New York, going up as far as the fields in Pelham. He did well. In three months he was able to repay his brothers and he was able, as well, to manage some of the English. He knew enough English to know that people were all talking about the gold that had been found far away, in California.

Willi and Jacob said that California was as far away as the moon.

"But they say they pick up money in the streets," said Levi.

"If California is as far away as we think, we are sure it doesn't have streets. Why, a man has to sail around two continents to reach it. By the time we could get there, the gold would long ago have been picked up."

"I am not talking about gold in bricks," said Levi. "Thousands of men are going there. They go with picks and shovels and mules and compasses. Do they think of needles and thread?"

Willi and Jacob gasped.

"Do they even think where they will live? Of course not. They think San Francisco is like the city they have left, that there are stores to sell them what they need. I think if I took needles and thread and thimbles and scissors and canvas to the gold fields I would make my fortune."

"But California is so far away," said Jacob, almost moaning.

"So was New York far away from Bad Ocheim. But it is not so far away as it once was, not with the clipper ships. And soon New York will have more than its share of peddlers. California does not. As long as there is gold, there will be cities, and I think that I, for one, would like to help build them."

"Have we not a good life here?" asked Willi. "Are we not comfortable? Do we not make ends meet? Yes, there will be more and more peddlers, but already we greet by name the housewives we sell to."

"I have learned this," said Levi. "Since I have come to America I find it is of two minds. It is both a place of opportunity and a place of great risk, and the two go hand in hand. I want to be what they call a Yankee, a man not afraid of moving. I want to go to the California gold fields."

Go he did.

On a fall day, he and Willi and Jacob went to the pier and there they stored their inventory in the ship's hold. They had specially ordered the canvas which came from the French manufacturing town of Nîmes and was called, "serge de Nîmes," but which Levi found Americans, with their quick speech, invariably called, "de Nîmes," or more simply "denim."

As the ship left with the evening tide, he waved good-bye to his brothers who called to him in English, "Good luck. Good luck."

He was just as seasick this time as he was the first time. And this was a longer voyage, with more ports of call. The clipper stopped at Charleston, South Carolina, and at Rio de Janeiro, and after rounding the southern tip of South America, it stopped at Lima, Peru, and on up the Mexican and Californian coast until it berthed at San Francisco. It was the spring of 1852.

The ship dropped anchor in the harbor one night and

waited. On the shore Levi could see the lights of homes, and land-based laughter floated out gently from the wharves. The smell of trees and earth was in the air, and Levi wondered why the ship had to wait out the night so far from shore.

In the morning he knew. As soon as dawn broke, dozens of small boats put out from shore. Some were boats fitted with crude sails, others made their way across the water with oarsmen. All of them converged about the ship, and the men in them began calling for news of the East. On the ship, men began calling out the name of the new President elected two years before.

There were others who pleaded to come aboard to inspect the merchandise which they knew the new immigrants to California had brought with them. Levi felt a surge of anticipation. The people came out to the very ship to buy! He and the other merchants and peddlers who had made the long voyage hurried to the crew and asked them to bring up their goods from the hold.

Slowly the big ship eased into the berth and by late afternoon Levi was ashore, waiting to claim his several rolls of denim. There was a hotel nearby and Levi decided to take a room for the night.

Levi had a little over three hundred dollars, most of it in gold, which weighed him down. Imagine his surprise when he found it took five dollars for that one night's lodging. He realized then why he saw men curled up along the wharves and the streets and under the trees, wrapped in blankets.

In the morning he was in for a bigger disappointment. He had intended to buy a small wagon in which to store his denim and to load new merchandise; but there was no supply house in all of San Francisco. He could not buy any peddlers' supplies of any kind. He understood now why there was such a heavy cargo. He was also dismayed to find that the needles which he sold the day before for twenty-five cents were selling for as high as two dollars—and a single egg cost a dollar. He was a greenhorn after all! He had thought that peddling through the fields of New Jersey and Pennsylvania and New York had cured him of his innocence but he was wrong. Yet if he was still a greenhorn, so were the native-born who had also sold their goods too cheap. Small consolation. Everything that came to San Francisco was shipped by boat or wagon train. There was no manufacturing or produce at all in the wild city. A pick and shovel and a mule cost two hundred dollars, although Levi found that the hardware owners would "grubstake" a man. They would outfit him with pick and shovel and mule and flour and his food, in return for half of all the gold he panned. They were pretty sure of their return since it was impossible for a man to resupply himself out of the woods itself. The grubstakers simply put waivers on all claims at the Land Office registered by their debtors. Levi found, after a morning of cold worry, they would do the same for a peddler.

One of them asked Levi what he had to sell and Levi answered denim canvas. The supplier thought hard about it and then turned Levi down, after Levi had hauled his denim to the store. The denim was not quite taut enough for tenting. In the end, Levi had to part with fifty dollars to purchase a wagon so he could transport his denim, all several rolls of it, through the city streets.

So he was in San Francisco with denim he couldn't sell and a wagon which had cost a good portion of his fast diminishing money and with no way to re-equip himself to make his living.

He started pushing his wagon through the muddy street. It was rough going. The spring thaw had made the street a quagmire. Sometimes Levi had to drop the handles of his wagon and put his shoulder to a wheel to get it over a bad place. Sometimes he had to transport his denim to the wooden sidewalk so he could lift his wagon from where it had bogged down, carry it to a dry spot, and reload his goods. He was trying to reach the trail that started the miners off toward the gold fields and it took him the better part of the day to reach that point.

The first day at his station, Levi sold nothing. He spent a chilly night outdoors and waked at dawn to watch the new stream of miners start by.

None of them this morning stopped at the place of the German immigrant. Few stopped anywhere. Now and then, they halted and inspected the wares laid before them and occasionally bought.

The first man to stop at Levi's wagon in the afternoon was a returning miner. He rode a sway-backed horse and he reined it before Levi's wagon and looked at the denim.

"Whatcha selling there, young fellow?" he asked.

"Tenting," said Levi.

"Don't need no tenting," said the man. "Need pants." He nudged his horse and started off, but Levi stopped him. "I can make you pants. I can make you pants from this that will last you."

"Okay, young fellow," said the man, dismounting. "I'll buy a pair of pants. I'm a sourdough and I need pants up in my diggins."

"What's a sourdough?" asked Levi.

"Why, it's a feller digs or pans for gold. Call us sourdoughs because that's what we eat. Fry ourselves some flour mixed with water."

When the sourdough dismounted, Levi saw readily enough why he needed pants. The pants he wore were out at the seat, and on both knees the patches had come loose.

"Never thought of making pants from tenting," said the sourdough, handling the denim.

"Neither did I," said Levi, "till I saw you."

The sourdough threw his head back and laughed. "Reckon that makes us even," he said.

Levi had no tape measure, but he had some string. He wrapped it around the sourdough's waist, and when he started to measure the inseam the man stopped him, and said, "You make 'em long so I'll have patching material. I'll roll 'em up." Levi followed the man's instructions.

"How much these pants gonna cost me?" asked the sourdough.

Levi did some mental arithmetic and said, "Six dollars."

"Ain't got no six dollars," said the sourdough. "But I got a good pinch of gold dust." He dug into his saddle bags and extracted a small leather pouch identical with the one in which he kept his tobacco that he chewed constantly as though it were food. Levi wondered if he ever got the two pouches mixed up and instead of tobacco stuffed his mouth with gold? The miner extended a good pinch of gold to Levi but the young man shook his head. "We have to go into San Francisco and have the pants cut."

"I need them pants now," said the miner, snatching back his gold and stuffing it into his pouch.

Levi had not been a peddler for nothing. He pointed patiently to San Francisco a mile away and said, just as if he had said it many times before, "We have simply to go into the city and have the pants cut. These are custom-tailored pants as befits a man with gold dust, and you will wear them before nightfall."

Once more Levi struggled with the wagon through the muddy ruts back to the city. The sourdough rode beside him, watching with the casual contempt of the plainsman the incredible struggle of the man of the city. Levi was certain that if the time came when he had to mount a horse he would be frightened of it. Right now he was more concerned with the prospects of finding a tailor than he was with his Herculean labors. He didn't know how much patience the sourdough had.

But he found a tailor and on sudden inspiration, Levi asked him to cut up all the tenting into pants, paying the tailor with the gold dust the miner gave him.

Thus when once again he ventured from the city, he went with a wagon filled with pants, all of which he sold that day. But selling the denim pants was no trick, no fortuitous occurrence. There were no work pants for sale in San Francisco. There were fine clothes, to be sure, and beaver coats and top hats, but there were no proper clothes for the prospectors, clothes that would stand the wear and tear of work at placer mining and mountain digging.

Levi Strauss opened a store on California Street in San Francisco, and proceeded immediately to improve his denim pants. Levi had equipped the pants with pockets, which the sourdoughs stuffed with nuggets they called "specimens," and which they brought back to the assay office to have examined for gold content. The pockets barely survived one trip, the weight of the "specimens" soon had them torn and flapping. One of these sourdoughs had a blacksmith rivet the back pockets with black iron nails. When Levi heard about it, he was struck with how good an idea it was. He experimented and found that a copper rivet did the trick better. After that, his pants were strengthened with copper rivets at all points of strain. He was selling a strong pair of pants which were like no other pants in the entire world.

It was not unusual in the years that followed for miners, then lumbermen, then cowboys, then farmers to come into his store and ask for a pair of "them pants of Levi's." In this manner did Levi Strauss become part of the West—by lending it his name.

Eventually his pants, which he had sold to a tattered sourdough on a sudden inspiration, became synonymous with the West itself. To this day, who is there who does not know what Levis are? Though Levi outgrew the desire to clothe himself in beaver and wear polished boots, he could have worn such clothes every day had he chosen. He made jeans and made them well. His business flourished and by the time he left this earth he was so much a part of San Francisco that half the front page of the morning newspaper was devoted to his obituary. And one hundred years after Levi Strauss left Germany, the company he founded was back in Europe with a warehouse at Antwerp distributing Levis in the European Common Market.

Levi has become part of our tradition, and though English remained perplexing to him until he died, no one ever could say that the man who made Levis wasn't authentically American.

DAEDALUS AND ICARUS

by Rex Warner

The wife of Minos, the great king of Crete, was the mother of a strange monster, half bull, half man, who was called the Minotaur. Wishing to hide away this disgrace to his family, Minos employed a famous Greek engineer, Daedalus, to make an enclosure so full of winding difficult passages that the monster could safely be shut up inside and would never find his way out. So Daedalus constructed the famous labyrinth, a maze of such size and with so many deceptive paths that, when the work was over, he himself could hardly find his way back to the main entrance.

When Daedalus had finished building the labyrinth, he wished to return to his home in Greece, but he was so useful as an inventor that Minos refused to let him go. So he and his son Icarus were compelled to stay in Crete against their will.

Finally Daedalus, hating his long exile and longing more and more to see his native country from which he was cut off by a long stretch of sea, said to himself: "Though Minos has blocked all my ways of escape by land and by water, there is certainly a way through the sky. That is the way I must go. I admit that he is supreme everywhere else, but he does not rule over the air."

Then he set his mind to work on problems that had never been thought about before, and succeeded in altering the very nature of things. He took feathers and arranged them in a row, beginning with the smallest ones and putting the bigger ones next, so that they looked as though they had grown in the shape of a wing. It was the same method as that by which the country Pan-pipes are made out of reeds of different lengths, fastened together. He tied the feathers together in the middle with twine, and joined them at the base with wax. Then, when they were arranged and fastened, he gave them all a slight bend, so that they looked exactly like the wings of real birds.

While he was working his son Icarus stood and watched him. Sometimes, laughing, he went chasing after a feather that the passing breeze blew away; sometimes he pressed his thumbs into the balls of yellow wax. He did not realize that what he was touching was going to be very dangerous to him, and by his playfulness he kept on interrupting the wonderful work on which his father was engaged.

When Daedalus had given the finishing touches to his invention, he put on his wings, flapped them up and down and hung poised in the air above the ground. Then he gave his son careful instructions about how to fly. "My advice to you, Icarus," he said, "is to fly at a moderate height. If you go too low, the sea water will weigh the feathers down; if you go too high, the heat of the sun will melt the wax. So you must fly neither too high nor too low. The best thing is to follow me."

While he gave him this advice, he was fitting the strange new wings to his son's shoulders, and, as he did so, tears ran down his aged cheeks and his hands trembled. He kissed his son for what was fated to be the last time, and then, taking to the air, he flew on ahead, anxious for the boy, like a bird which for the first time leads his fledglings out of their high nest into the yielding air. He called out words of encouragement to the boy and taught him to use those fatal wings, constantly looking back, as he flapped his own wings, to see how his son was managing.

On the ground people fishing with long trembling rods, or shepherds leaning on their crooks, or plowmen bent over their plow handles looked up at them in astonishment and came to the conclusion that, since they were flying through the air, they must be gods.

And now they had left several islands—Delos and Paros —behind them. Juno's sacred island of Samos was on the left, and on the right was Calymne, famous for its honey. At this point the boy began to enjoy the daring experience of flight. Longing for the open sky, he forgot to follow his father and climbed higher and higher in the air. As he came nearer to the sun, the scorching rays began to soften the wax that kept the feathers together. The wax melted and Icarus found that he was flapping bare arms which, without their wings, had no hold upon the air. He fell, and the blue sea, which is still called the Icarian Sea, closed over his lips, as he cried out for his father. Unhappy Daedalus, a father no longer, also cried out. "Icarus!" he called, "Where are you? Where have you gone to?" As he was crying out the boy's name, he saw the wings floating on the water. Then he cursed his own invention, found his son's body and buried it. The land is still called after the name of the buried boy.

A group of astronauts chosen for a real flight in space

Antaeus

by Borden Deal

This was during the wartime, when lots of people were coming North for jobs in factories and war industries, when people moved around a lot more than they do now and sometimes kids were thrown into new groups and new lives that were completely different from anything they had ever known before. I remember this one kid, T.J. his name was, from somewhere down South, whose family moved into our building during that time. They'd come North with everything they owned piled into the back seat of an old-model sedan that you wouldn't expect could make the trip, with T.J. and his three younger sisters riding shakily on top of the load of junk.

Our building was just like all the others there, with families crowded into a few rooms, and I guess there were twenty-five or thirty kids about my age in that one building. Of course, there were a few of us who formed a gang and ran together all the time after school, and I was the one who brought T.J. in and started the whole thing.

The building right next door to us was a factory where they made walking dolls. It was a low building with a flat, tarred roof that had a parapet all around it about head-high and we'd found out a long time before that no one, not even the watchman, paid any attention to the roof because it was higher than any of the other buildings around. So my gang used the roof as a headquarters. We could get up there by crossing over to the fire escape from our own roof on a plank and then going on up. It was a secret place for us, where nobody else could go without our permission.

I remember the day I first took T.J. up there to meet the gang. He was a stocky, robust kid with a shock of white hair, nothing sissy about him except his voice—he talked in this slow, gentle voice like you never heard before. He talked different from any of us and you noticed it right away. But I liked him anyway, so I told him to come on up.

We climbed up over the parapet and dropped down on the roof. The rest of the gang were already there.

"Hi," I said. I jerked my thumb at T.J. "He just moved into the building yesterday."

He just stood there, not scared or anything, just looking, like the first time you see somebody you're not sure you're going to like.

"Hi," Blackie said. "Where are you from?"

"Marion County," T.J. said.

We laughed. "Marion County?" I said. "Where's that?"

He looked at me for a moment like I was a stranger, too. "It's in Alabama," he said, like I ought to know where it was.

"What's your name?" Charley said.

"T.J.," he said, looking back at him. He had pale blue eyes that looked washed-out but he looked directly at Charley, waiting for his reaction. He'll be all right, I thought. No sissy in him . . . except that voice. Who ever talked like that?

"T.J.," Blackie said. "That's just initials. What's your real name? Nobody in the world has just initials."

"I do," he said. "And they're T.J. That's all the name I got."

His voice was resolute with the knowledge of his rightness and for a moment no one had anything to say. T.J. looked around at the rooftop and down at the black tar under his feet. "Down yonder where I come from," he said, "we played out in the woods. Don't you-all have no woods around here?"

"Naw," Blackie said. "There's the park a few blocks over, but it's full of kids and cops and old women. You can't do a thing."

T.J. kept looking at the tar under his feet. "You mean you ain't got no fields to raise nothing in? . . . no watermelons or nothing?"

"Naw," I said scornfully. "What do you want to grow something for? The folks can buy everything they need at the store."

He looked at me again with that strange, unknowing look. "In Marion County," he said, "I had my own acre of cotton and my own acre of corn. It was mine to plant and make ever' year."

He sounded like it was something to be proud of, and in some obscure way it made the rest of us angry. . . . "Who'd want to have their own acre of cotton and corn?" Blackie said. "That's just work. What can you do with an acre of cotton and corn?"

T.J. looked at him. "Well, you get part of the bale offen your acre," he said seriously. "And I fed my acre of corn to my calf."

We didn't really know what he was talking about, so we were more puzzled than angry; otherwise, I guess, we'd have chased him off the roof and wouldn't let him be part of our gang. But he was strange and different and we were all attracted by his stolid sense of rightness and belonging, maybe by the strange softness of his voice contrasting our own tones of speech into harshness.

He moved his foot against the black tar. "We could make our own field right here," he said softly, thoughtfully.

"Come spring we could raise us what we want to . . . watermelons and garden truck and no telling what all."

"You'd have to be a good farmer to make these tar roofs grow watermelons," I said. We all laughed.

But T.J. looked serious. "We could haul us some dirt up here," he said. "And spread it out even and water it and before you know it we'd have us a crop in here." He looked at us intently. "Wouldn't that be fun?"

"They wouldn't let us," Blackie said quickly.

"I thought you said this was you-all's roof," T.J. said to me. "That you-all could do anything you wanted to up here."

"They've never bothered us," I said. I felt the idea beginning to catch fire in me. It was a big idea and it took a while for it to sink in but the more I thought about it the better I liked it. "Say," I said to the gang. "He might have something there. Just make us a regular roof garden, with flowers and grass and trees and everything. And all ours, too," I said. "We wouldn't let anybody up here except the ones we wanted to."

"It'd take a while to grow trees," T.J. said quickly, but we weren't paying any attention to him. They were all talking about it suddenly, all excited with the idea after I'd put it in a way they could catch hold of it. Only rich people had roof gardens, we knew, and the idea of our own private domain excited them.

"We could bring it up in sacks and boxes," Blackie said. "We'd have to do it while the folks weren't paying any attention to us, for we'd have to come up to the roof of our building and then cross over with it."

"Where could we get the dirt?" somebody said worriedly.

"Out of those vacant lots over close to school," Blackie said. "Nobody'd notice if we scraped it up."

I slapped T.J. on the shoulder. "Man, you had a wonderful idea," I said, and everybody grinned at him, remembering that he had started it. "Our own private roof garden."

He grinned back. "It'll be ourn," he said. "All ourn." Then he looked thoughtful again. "Maybe I can lay my hands on some cotton seed, too. You think we could raise us some cotton?"

We'd started big projects before at one time or another, like any gang of kids, but they'd always petered out for lack of organization and direction. But this one didn't . . . somehow or other T.J. kept it going all through the winter months. He kept talking about the watermelons and the cotton we'd raise, come spring, and when even that wouldn't work he'd switch around to my idea of flowers and grass and trees, though he was always honest enough to add that it'd take a while to get any trees started. He always had it on his mind and he'd mention it in school, getting them lined up to carry dirt that afternoon, saying in a casual way that he reckoned a few more weeks ought to see the job through.

Our little area of private earth grew slowly. T.J. was smart enough to start in one corner of the building, heaping up the carried earth two or three feet thick, so that we had an immediate result to look at, to contemplate with awe. Some of the evenings T.J. alone was carrying earth up to the building, the rest of the gang distracted by other enterprises or interests, but T.J. kept plugging along on his own and eventually we'd all come back to him again and then our own little acre would grow more rapidly.

He was careful about the kind of dirt he'd let us carry up there and more than once he dumped a sandy load over the parapet into the areaway below because it wasn't good enough. He found out the kinds of earth in all the vacant lots for blocks around. He'd pick it up and feel it and smell it, frozen though it was sometimes, and then he'd

149

say it was good growing soil or it wasn't worth anything and we'd have to go somewhere else.

Thinking about it now, I don't see how he kept us at it. It was hard work, lugging paper sacks and boxes of dirt all the way up the stairs of our own building, keeping out of the way of the grownups so they wouldn't catch on to what we were doing. They probably wouldn't have cared, for they didn't pay much attention to us, but we wanted to keep it secret anyway. Then we had to go through the trap door to our roof, teeter over a plank to the fire escape, then climb two or three stories to the parapet and drop down onto the roof. All that for a small pile of earth that sometimes didn't seem worth the effort. But T.J. kept the vision bright within us, his words shrewd and calculated toward the fulfillment of his dream; and he worked harder than any of us. He seemed driven toward a goal that we couldn't see, a particular point in time that would be definitely marked by signs and wonders that only he could see.

The laborious earth just lay there during the cold months, inert and lifeless, the clods lumpy and cold under our feet when we walked over it. But one day it rained and afterward there was a softness in the air and the earth was live and giving again with moisture and warmth. That evening T.J. smelled the air, his nostrils dilating with the odor of the earth under his feet.

"It's spring," he said, and there was a gladness rising in his voice that filled us all with the same feeling. "It's mighty late for it, but it's spring. I'd just about decided it wasn't never gonna get here at all."

We were all sniffing at the air, too, trying to smell it the way that T.J. did, and I can still remember the sweet odor of the earth under our feet. It was the first time in my life that spring and spring earth had meant anything to me. I looked at T.J. then, knowing in a faint way the hunger within him through the toilsome winter months, knowing the dream that lay behind his plan. He was a new Antaeus, preparing his own bed of strength.

"Planting time," he said. "We'll have to find us some seed."

"What do we do?" Blackie said. "How do we do it?"

"First we'll have to break up the clods," T.J. said. "That won't be hard to do. Then we plant the seed and after a while they come up. Then you got you a crop." He frowned. "But you ain't got it raised yet. You got to tend it and hoe it and take care of it and all the time it's growing and growing, while you're awake and while you're asleep. Then you lay it by when it's growed and let it ripen and then you got you a crop."

"There's those wholesale seed houses over on Sixth," I said. "We could probably swipe some grass seed over there."

T.J. looked at the earth. "You-all seem mighty set on raising some grass," he said. "I ain't never put no effort into that. I spent all my life trying not to raise grass."

"But it's pretty," Blackie said. "We could play on it and take sunbaths on it. Like having our own lawn. Lots of people got lawns."

"Well," T.J. said. He looked at the rest of us, hesitant for the first time. He kept on looking at us for a moment. "I did have it in mind to raise some corn and vegetables. But we'll plant grass."

He was smart. He knew where to give in. And I don't suppose it made any difference to him, really. He just wanted to grow something, even if it was grass.

"Of course," he said, "I do think we ought to plant a row of watermelons. They'd be mighty nice to eat while we was a-laying on that grass."

We all laughed. "All right," I said. "We'll plant us a row of watermelons."

Things went very quickly then. Perhaps half the roof was

covered with the earth, the half that wasn't broken by ventilators, and we swiped pocketfuls of grass seed from the open bins in the wholesale seed house, mingling among the buyers on Saturdays and during the school lunch hour. T.J. showed us how to prepare the earth, breaking up the clods and smoothing it and sowing the grass seed. It looked rich and black now with moisture, receiving of the seed, and it seemed that the grass sprang up overnight, pale green in the early spring.

We couldn't keep from looking at it, unable to believe that we had created this delicate growth. We looked at T.J. with understanding now, knowing the fulfillment of the plan he had carried alone within his mind. We had worked without full understanding of the task but he had known all the time.

We found that we couldn't walk on the delicate blades, as we expected to, but we didn't mind. It was enough just to look at it, to realize that it was the work of our own hands, and each evening the whole gang was there, trying to measure the growth that had been achieved that day.

One time a foot was placed on the plot of ground . . . one time only, Blackie stepped onto it with sudden bravado. Then he looked at the crushed blades and there was shame in his face. He did not do it again. This was his grass, too, and not to be desecrated. No one said anything, for it was not necessary.

T.J. had reserved a small section for watermelons and he was still trying to find some seed for it. The wholesale house didn't have any watermelon seed and we didn't know where we could lay our hands on them. T.J. shaped the earth into mounds, ready to receive them, three mounds lying in a straight line along the edge of the grass plot.

We had just about decided that we'd have to buy the

seed if we were to get them. It was a violation of our principles, but we were anxious to get the watermelons started. Somewhere or other, T.J. got his hands on a seed catalogue and brought it one evening to our roof garden.

"We can order them now," he said, showing us the catalogue. "Look!"

We all crowded around, looking at the fat, green watermelons pictured in full color on the pages. Some of them were split open, showing the red, tempting meat, making our mouths water.

"Now we got to scrape up some seed money," T.J. said, looking at us. "I got a quarter. How much you-all got?"

We made up a couple of dollars between us and T.J. nodded his head. "That'll be more than enough. Now we got to decide what kind to get. I think them Kleckley Sweets. What do you-all think?"

He was going into esoteric matters beyond our reach. We hadn't even known there were different kinds of melons. So we just nodded our heads and agreed that Yes, we thought the Kleckley Sweets too.

"I'll order them tonight," T.J. said. "We ought to have them in a few days."

"What are you boys doing up here?" an adult voice said behind us.

It startled us, for no one had ever come up here before, in all the time we had been using the roof of the factory. We jerked around and saw three men standing near the trap door at the other end of the roof. They weren't policemen, or night watchmen, but three men in plump business suits, looking at us. They walked toward us.

"What are you boys doing up here?" the one in the middle said again.

We stood still, guilt heavy among us, levied by the tone of voice, and looked at the three strangers.

The men stared at the grass flourishing behind us. "What's this?" the man said. "How did this get up here?"

"Sure is growing good, ain't it?" T.J. said conversationally. "We planted it."

The men kept looking at the grass as if they didn't believe it. It was a thick carpet over the earth now, a patch of deep greenness startling in the sterile industrial surroundings.

"Yes sir," T.J. said proudly. "We toted that earth up here and planted that grass." He fluttered the seed catalogue. "And we're just fixing to plant us some watermelon."

The man looked at him then, his eyes strange and faraway. "What do you mean, putting this on the roof of my building?" he said. "Do you want to go to jail?"

T.J. looked shaken. The rest of us were silent, frightened by the authority of his voice. We had grown up aware of adult authority, of policemen and night watchmen and teachers, and this man sounded like all the others. But it was a new thing to T.J.

"Well, you wan't using the roof," T.J. said. He paused a moment and added shrewdly, "So we just thought to pretty it up a little bit."

"And sag it so I'd have to rebuild it," the man said sharply. He started turning away, saying to another man beside him, "See that all that junk is shoveled off by tomorrow."

"Yes sir," the man said.

T.J. started forward. "You can't do that," he said. "We toted it up here and it's our earth. We planted it and raised it and toted it up here."

The man stared at him coldly. "But it's my building," he said. "It's to be shoveled off tomorrow."

"It's our earth," T.J. said desperately. "You ain't got no right!"

The men walked on without listening and descended

clumsily through the trap door. T.J. stood looking after them, his body tense with anger, until they had disappeared. They wouldn't even argue with him, wouldn't let him defend his earth-rights.

He turned to us. "We won't let 'em do it," he said fiercely. "We'll stay up here all day tomorrow and the day after that and we won't let 'em do it."

We just looked at him. We knew that there was no stopping it. He saw it in our faces and his face wavered for a moment before he gripped it into determination.

"They ain't got no right," he said. "It's our earth. It's our land. Can't nobody touch a man's own land."

We kept on looking at him, listening to the words but knowing that it was no use. The adult world had descended on us even in our richest dream and we knew there was no calculating the adult world, no fighting it, no winning against it.

We started moving slowly toward the parapet and the fire escape, avoiding a last look at the green beauty of the earth that T.J. had planted for us . . . had planted deeply in our minds as well as in our experience. We filed slowly over the edge and down the steps to the plank, T.J. coming last, and all of us could feel the weight of his grief behind us.

"Wait a minute," he said suddenly, his voice harsh with the effort of calling. We stopped and turned, held by the tone of his voice, and looked up at him standing above us on the fire escape.

"We can't stop them?" he said, looking down at us, his face strange in the dusky light. "There ain't no way to stop 'em?"

"No," Blackie said with finality. "They own the building."

We stood still for a moment, looking up at T.J., caught into inaction by the decision working in his face. He stared back at us and his face was pale and mean in the poor light, with a bald nakedness in his skin like cripples have sometimes.

"They ain't gonna touch my earth," he said fiercely. "They ain't gonna lay a hand on it! Come on."

He turned around and started up the fire escape again, almost running against the effort of climbing. We followed more slowly, not knowing what he intended. By the time we reached him, he had seized a board and thrust it into the soil, scooping it up and flinging it over the parapet into the areaway below. He straightened and looked at us.

"They can't touch it," he said. "I won't let 'em lay a dirty hand on it!"

We saw it then. He stooped to his labor again and we followed, the gusts of his anger moving in frenzied labor among us as we scattered along the edge of earth, scooping it and throwing it over the parapet, destroying with anger the growth we had nurtured with such tender care. The soil carried so laboriously upward to the light and the sun cascaded swiftly into the dark areaway, the green glades of grass crumpled and twisted in the falling.

It took less time than you would think . . . the task of destruction is infinitely easier than that of creation. We stopped at the end, leaving only a scattering of loose soil, and when it was finally over a stillness stood among the group and over the factory building. We looked down at the bare sterility of black tar, felt the harsh texture of it under the soles of our shoes, and the anger had gone out of us, leaving only a sore aching in our minds like overstretched muscles.

T.J. stood for a moment, his breathing slowing from anger and effort, caught into the same contemplation of destruction as all of us. He stooped slowly, finally, and picked up a lonely blade of grass left trampled under our feet and put it between his teeth, tasting it, sucking the greenness out of it into his mouth. Then he started walking toward the fire escape, moving before any of us were ready to move, and disappeared over the edge.

We followed him but he was already halfway down to the ground, going on past the board where we crossed over, climbing down into the areaway. We saw the last section swing down with his weight and then he stood on the concrete below us, looking at the small pile of anonymous earth scattered by our throwing. Then he walked across the place where we could see him and disappeared toward the street without glancing back, without looking up to see us watching him.

They did not find him for two weeks. Then the Nashville police caught him just outside the Nashville freight yards. He was walking along the railroad track; still heading south, still heading home.

As for us, who had no remembered home to call us . . . none of us ever again climbed the escape-way to the roof.

THE IMPOSSIBLE DREAM

from the musical play, "Man of La Mancha"
Words by: Joe Darion — Music by: Mitch Leigh

To dream the impossible dream,
To fight the unbeatable foe,
To bear with unbearable sorrow,
To run where the brave dare not go.

To right the unrightable wrong,
To love pure and chaste from afar,
To try when your arms are too weary,
To reach the unreachable star!

This is my quest, to follow that star,
No matter how hopeless, no matter how far;
To fight for the right without question or pause,
To be willing to march into hell for a heavenly cause!

And I know, if I'll only be true
To this glorious quest,
That my heart will lie peaceful and calm,
When I'm laid to my rest,
And the world will be better for this;
That one man, scorned and covered with scars,
Still strove with his last ounce of courage,
To reach the unreachable stars.

MANHOOD

by John Wain

Swiftly free-wheeling, their breath coming easily, the
man and the boy steered their bicycles down the short dip
which led them from woodland into open country. Then they
looked ahead and saw that the road began to climb.

"Now, Rob," said Mr. Willison, settling his plump
haunches firmly on the saddle, "just up that rise and we'll
get off and have a good rest."

"Can't we rest now?" the boy asked. "My legs feel all
funny. As if they're turning to water."

"Rest at the top," said Mr. Willison firmly. "Remember
what I told you? The first thing any athlete has to learn is
to break the fatigue barrier."

"I've broken it already. I was feeling tired when we were
going along the main road and I—"

"When fatigue sets in, the thing to do is to keep going
until it wears off. Then you get your second wind and your
second endurance."

"I've already done that."

"Up we go," said Mr. Willison, "and at the top we'll have
a good rest." He panted slightly and stood on his pedals,
causing his machine to sway from side to side in a labored

manner. Rob, falling silent, pushed doggedly at his pedals. Slowly, the pair wavered up the straight road to the top. Once there, Mr. Willison dismounted with exaggerated steadiness, laid his bicycle carefully on its side, and spread his jacket on the ground before sinking down to rest. Rob slid hastily from the saddle and flung himself full-length on the grass.

"Don't lie there," said his father. "You'll catch cold."

"I'm all right. I'm warm."

"Come and sit on this. When you're overheated, that's just when you're prone to—"

"I'm all *right*, Dad. I want to lie here. My back aches."

"Your back needs strengthening, that's why it aches. It's a pity we don't live near a river where you could get some rowing."

The boy did not answer, and Mr. Willison, aware that he was beginning to sound like a nagging, overanxious parent, allowed himself to be defeated and did not press the suggestion about Rob's coming to sit on his jacket. Instead, he waited a moment and then glanced at his watch.

"Twenty to twelve. We must get going in a minute."

"*What?* I thought we were going to have a rest."

"Well, we're having one, aren't we?" said Mr. Willison reasonably. "I've got my breath back, so surely you must have."

"My back still aches. I want to lie here a bit."

"Sorry," said Mr. Willison, getting up and moving over to his bicycle. "We've got at least twelve miles to do and lunch is at one."

"Dad, why did we have to come so far if we've got to get back for one o'clock? I know, let's find a telephone box and ring up Mum and tell her we—"

"Nothing doing. There's no reason why two fit men shouldn't cycle twelve miles in an hour and ten minutes."

"But we've already done about a million miles."

"We've done about fourteen, by my estimation," said Mr. Willison stiffly. "What's the good of going for a bike ride if you don't cover a bit of distance?"

He picked up his bicycle and stood waiting. Rob, with his hand over his eyes, lay motionless on the grass. His legs looked thin and white among the rich grass.

"Come on, Rob."

The boy showed no sign of having heard. Mr. Willison got on to his bicycle and began to ride slowly away. "Rob," he called over his shoulder, "I'm going."

Rob lay like a sullen corpse by the roadside. He looked horribly like the victim of an accident, unmarked but dead from internal injuries. Mr. Willison cycled fifty yards, then a hundred, then turned in a short, irritable circle and came back to where his son lay.

"Rob, is there something the matter or are you just being awkward?"

The boy removed his hand and looked up into his father's face. His eyes were surprisingly mild: there was no fire of rebellion in them.

"I'm tired and my back aches. I can't go on yet."

"Look, Rob," said Mr. Willison gently, "I wasn't going to tell you this, because I meant it to be a surprise, but when you get home you'll find a present waiting for you."

"What kind of present?"

"Something very special I've bought for you. The man's coming this morning to fix it up. That's one reason why I suggested a bike ride this morning. He'll have done it by now."

"What is it?"

"Aha. It's a surprise. Come on, get on your bike and let's go home and see."

Rob sat up, then slowly clambered to his feet. "Isn't there a short cut home?"

"I'm afraid not. It's only twelve miles."

Rob said nothing.

162

"And a lot of that's downhill," Mr. Willison added brightly. His own legs were tired and his muscles fluttered unpleasantly. In addition, he suddenly realized he was very thirsty. Rob, still without speaking, picked up his bicycle, and they pedalled away.

"Where is he?" Mrs. Willison asked, coming into the garage.

"Gone up to his room," said Mr. Willison. He doubled his fist and gave the punch-ball a thudding blow. "Seems to have fixed it pretty firmly. You gave him the instructions, I suppose."

"What's he doing up in his room? It's lunch-time."

"He said he wanted to rest a bit."

"I hope you're satisfied," said Mrs. Willison. "A lad of thirteen, nearly fourteen years of age, just when he should have a really big appetite, and when the lunch is put on the table he's *resting*—"

"Now look, I know what I'm—"

"Lying down in his room, resting, too tired to eat because you've dragged him up hill and down dale on one of your—"

"We did nothing that couldn't be reasonably expected of a boy of his age."

"How do you know?" Mrs. Willison demanded. "You never did anything of that kind when you were a boy. How do you know what can be reasonably—"

"Now look," said Mr. Willison again. "When I was a boy, it was study, study, study all the time, with the fear of unemployment and insecurity in everybody's mind. I was never even given a bicycle. I never boxed, I never rowed, I never did anything to develop my physique. It was just work, work, work, pass this exam, get that certificate. Well, I did it and now I'm qualified and in a secure job. But you know as well as I do that they let me down. Nobody encouraged me to build myself up."

"Well, what does it matter? You're all right—"

"Grace!" Mr. Willison interrupted sharply. "I am not all right and you know it. I am under average height, my chest is flat and I'm—"

"What nonsense. You're taller than I am and I'm—"

"No son of mine is going to grow up with the same wretched physical heritage that I—"

"No, he'll just have heart disease through overtaxing his strength, because you haven't got the common sense to—"

"His heart is one hundred per cent all right. Not three weeks have gone by since the doctor looked at him."

"Well, why does he get so over-tired if he's all right? Why is he lying down now instead of coming to the table, a boy of his age?"

A slender shadow blocked part of the dazzling sun in the doorway. Looking up simultaneously, the Willisons greeted their son.

"Lunch ready, Mum? I'm hungry."

"Ready when you are," Grace Willison beamed. "Just wash your hands and come to the table."

"Look, Rob," said Mr. Willison. "If you hit it with your left hand and then catch it on the rebound with your right, it's excellent ring training." He dealt the punchball two amateurish blows. "That's what they call a right cross," he said.

"I think it's fine. I'll have some fun with it," said Rob. He watched mildly as his father peeled off the padded mittens.

"Here, slip these on," said Mr. Willison. "They're just training gloves. They harden your fists. Of course, we can get a pair of proper gloves later. But these are specially for use with the ball."

"Lunch," called Mrs. Willison from the house.

"Take a punch at it," Mr. Willison urged.

"Let's go and eat."

"Go on. One punch before you go in. I haven't seen you hit it yet."

Rob took the gloves, put on the right-hand one, and gave the punchball one conscientious blow, aiming at the exact center. "Now let's go in," he said.

"Lunch!"

"All right. We're coming . . ."

"Five feet eight, Rob," said Mr. Willison, folding up the wooden ruler. "You're taller than I am. This is a great landmark."

"Only *just* taller."

"But you're growing all the time. Now all you have to do is to start growing outwards as well as upwards. We'll have you in the middle of that scrum. The heaviest forward in the pack."

Rob picked up his shirt and began uncertainly poking his arms into the sleeves.

"When do they pick the team?" Mr. Willison asked. "I should have thought they'd have done it by now."

"They have done it," said Rob. He bent down to pick up his socks from under a chair.

"They have? And you—"

"I wasn't selected," said the boy, looking intently at the socks as if trying to detect minute differences in color and weave.

Mr. Willison opened his mouth, closed it again, and stood for a moment looking out of the window. Then he gently laid his hand on his son's shoulder. "Bad luck," he said quietly.

"I tried hard," said Rob quickly.

"I'm sure you did."

"I played my hardest in the trial games."

"It's just bad luck," said Mr. Willison. "It could happen to anybody."

There was silence as they both continued with their dressing. A faint smell of frying rose into the air, and they could hear Mrs. Willison laying the table for breakfast.

"That's it, then, for this season," said Mr. Willison, as if to himself.

"I forgot to tell you, though," said Rob. "I was selected for the boxing team."

"You *were?* I didn't know the school had one."

"It's new. Just formed. They had some trials for it at the end of last term. I found my punching was better than most people's because I'd been getting plenty of practice with the ball."

Mr. Willison put out a hand and felt Rob's biceps. "Not bad, not bad at all," he said critically. "But if you're going to be a boxer and represent the school, you'll need more power up there. I tell you what. We'll train together."

"That'll be fun," said Rob. "I'm training at school too."

"What weight do they put you in?"

"It isn't weight, it's age. Under fifteen. Then when you get over fifteen you get classified into weights."

"Well," said Mr. Willison, tying his tie, "you'll be in a good position for the under-fifteens. You've got six months to play with. And there's no reason why you shouldn't steadily put muscle on all the time. I suppose you'll be entered as a team, for tournaments and things?"

"Yes. There's a big one at the end of next term. I'll be in that."

Confident, joking, they went down to breakfast. "Two eggs for Rob, Mum," said Mr. Willison. "He's in training. He's going to be a heavyweight."

"A heavyweight what?" Mrs. Willison asked, teapot in hand.

"Boxer," Rob smiled.

Grace Willison put down the teapot, her lips compressed, and looked from one to the other. "*Boxing?*" she repeated.

"Boxing," Mr. Willison replied calmly.

"Over my dead body," said Mrs. Willison. "That's one sport I'm definite that he's never going in for."

"Too late. They've picked him for the under-fifteens. He's had trials and everything."

"Is this true, Rob?" she demanded.

"Yes," said the boy, eating rapidly.

"Well, you can just tell them you're dropping it. Baroness Summerskill—"

"To hell with Baroness Summerskill!" her husband shouted. "The first time he gets a chance to do something, the first time he gets picked for a team and given a chance to show what he's made of, and you have to bring up Baroness Summerskill."

"But it injures their brains! All those blows on the front of the skull. I've read about it—"

"Injures their brains!" Mr. Willison snorted. "Has it injured Ingemar Johansson's brain? Why, he's one of the acutest businessmen in the world!"

"Rob," said Mrs. Willison steadily, "when you get to school, go and see the sports master and tell him you're giving up boxing."

"There isn't a sports master. All the masters do bits of it at different times."

"There must be one who's in charge of the boxing. All you have to do is tell him—"

"Are you ready, Rob?" said Mr. Willison. "You'll be late for school if you don't go."

"I'm in plenty of time, Dad. I haven't finished my breakfast."

"Never mind, push along, old son. You've had your egg and bacon, that's what matters. I want to talk to your mother."

Cramming a piece of dry toast into his mouth, the boy picked up his satchel and wandered from the room. Husband and wife sat back, glaring hot-eyed at each other.

The quarrel began, and continued for many days. In the end it was decided that Rob should continue boxing until he had represented the school at the tournament in March of the following year, and should then give it up.

"Ninety-six, ninety-seven, ninety-eight, ninety-nine, a hundred," Mr. Willison counted. "Right, that's it. Now go and take your shower and get into bed."

"I don't feel tired, honestly," Rob protested.

"Who's manager here, you or me?" Mr. Willison asked bluffly. "I'm in charge of training and you can't say my methods don't work. Fifteen solid weeks and you start questioning my decisions on the very night of the fight?"

"It just seems silly to go to bed when I'm not—"

"My dear Rob, please trust me. No boxer ever went into a big fight without spending an hour or two in bed, resting, just before going to his dressingroom."

"All right. But I bet none of the others are bothering to do all this."

"That's exactly why you're going to be better than the others. Now go and get your shower before you catch cold. Leave the skipping-rope, I'll put it away."

After Rob had gone, Mr. Willison folded the skipping-rope into a neat ball and packed it away in the case that contained the boy's gloves, silk dressing gown, lace-up boxing boots, and trunks with the school badge sewn into the correct position on the right leg. There would be no harm in a little skipping, to limber up and conquer his nervousness while waiting to go on. Humming, he snapped down the catches of the small leather case and went into the house.

Mrs. Willison did not lift her eyes from the television set as he entered. "All ready now, Mother," said Mr. Willison.

"He's going to rest in bed now, and go along at about six o'clock. I'll go with him and wait till the doors open to be sure of a ringside seat." He sat down on the sofa beside his wife, and tried to put his arm round her. "Come on, love," he said coaxingly, "Don't spoil my big night."

She turned to him and he was startled to see her eyes brimming with angry tears. "What about my big night?" she asked, her voice harsh. "Fourteen years ago, remember? When he came into the world."

"Well, what about it?" Mr. Willison parried, uneasily aware that the television set was quacking and signaling on the fringe of his attention, turning the scene from clumsy tragedy into a clumsier farce.

"Why didn't you tell me then?" she sobbed. "Why did you let me have a son if all you were interested in was having him punched to death by a lot of rough bullet-headed louts who—"

"Take a grip on yourself, Grace. A punch on the nose won't hurt him."

"You're an unnatural father," she keened. "I don't know how you can bear to send him into that ring to be beaten and thumped—Oh, why can't you stop him now? Keep him at home? There's no *law* that compels us to—"

"That's where you're wrong, Grace," said Mr. Willison sternly. "There is a law. The unalterable law of nature that says that the young males of the species indulge in manly trials of strength. Think of all the other lads who are going into the ring tonight. D'you think their mothers are sitting about crying and kicking up a fuss? No—they're proud to have strong, masculine sons who can stand up in the ring and take a few punches."

"Go away, please," said Mrs. Willison, sinking back with closed eyes. "Just go right away and don't come near me until it's all over."

"Grace!"

"Please. Please leave me alone. I can't bear to look at you and I can't bear to hear you."

"You're hysterical," said Mr. Willison bitterly. Rising, he went out into the hall and called up the stairs. "Are you in bed, Rob?"

There was a slight pause and then Rob's voice called faintly, "Could you come up, Dad?"

"Come up? Why? Is something the matter?"

"Could you come up?"

Mr. Willison ran up the stairs. "What is it?" he panted. "D'you want something?"

"I think I've got appendicitis," said Rob. He lay squinting among the pillows, his face suddenly narrow and crafty.

"I don't believe you," said Mr. Willison shortly. "I've supervised your training for fifteen weeks and I know you're as fit as a fiddle. You can't possibly have anything wrong with you."

"I've got a terrible pain in my side," said Rob. "Low down on the right-hand side. That's where appendicitis comes, isn't it?"

Mr. Willison sat down on the bed. "Listen, Rob," he said. "Don't do this to me. All I'm asking you to do is go into the ring and have this one bout. You've been picked for the school team and everyone's depending on you."

"I'll die if you don't get the doctor." Rob suddenly hissed. "Mum!" he shouted.

Mrs. Willison came bounding up the stairs. "What is it, my pet?"

"My stomach hurts. Low down on the right-hand side."

"Appendicitis!" She whirled to face Mr. Willison. "That's what comes of your foolishness!"

"I don't believe it," said Mr. Willison. He went out of the bedroom and down the stairs. The television was still jabbering in the living room, and for fifteen minutes Mr. Willison forced himself to sit staring at the strident puppets, glistening in metallic light, as they enacted their Lilliputian rituals. Then he went up to the bedroom again. Mrs. Willison was bathing Rob's forehead.

"His temperature's normal," she said.

"Of course his temperature's normal," said Mr. Willison. "He doesn't want to fight, that's all."

"Fetch the doctor," said a voice from under the cold flannel that swathed Rob's face.

"We will, pet, if you don't get better very soon," said Mrs. Willison, darting a murderous glance at her husband.

Mr. Willison slowly went downstairs. For a moment he stood looking at the telephone, then picked it up and dialled the number of the grammar school. No one answered. He replaced the receiver, went to the foot of the stairs and called, "What's the name of the master in charge of this tournament?"

"I don't know," Rob called weakly.

"You told me you'd been training with Mr. Granger," Mr. Willison called. "Would he know anything about it?"

Rob did not answer, so Mr. Willison looked up all the Grangers in the telephone book. There were four in the town, but only one was M.A. "That's him," said Mr. Willison. With lead in his heart and ice in his fingers, he dialled the number.

Mrs. Granger fetched Mr. Granger. Yes, he taught at the school. He was the right man. What could he do for Mr. Willison?

"It's about tonight's boxing tournament."

"Sorry, what? The line's bad."

"Tonight's boxing tournament."

"Have you got the right person?"

"You teach my son, Rob—we've just agreed on that. Well, it's about the boxing tournament he's supposed to be taking part in tonight."

"Where?"

"Where? At the school, of course. He's representing the under-fifteens."

There was a pause. "I'm not quite sure what mistake you're making, Mr. Willison, but I think you've got hold of the wrong end of at least one stick." A hearty, defensive laugh. "If Rob belongs to a boxing club it's certainly news to me, but in any case it can't be anything to do with the school. We don't go in for boxing."

"Don't go in for it?"

"We don't offer it. It's not in our curriculum."

"Oh," said Mr. Willison. "Oh. Thank you. I must have— well, thank you."

"Not at all. I'm glad to answer any queries. Everything's all right, I trust?"

"Oh, yes," said Mr. Willison, "yes, thanks. Everything's all right."

He put down the telephone, hesitated, then turned and began slowly to climb the stairs.

THE PARABLE OF THE EAGLE

by James Aggrey

A certain man went through a forest seeking any bird of interest he might find. He caught a young eagle, brought it home and put it among his fowls and ducks and turkeys, and gave it chickens' food to eat even though it was an eagle, the king of birds.

Five years later a naturalist came to see him and, after passing through his garden, said: "That bird is an eagle, not a chicken."

"Yes," said its owner, "but I have trained it to be a chicken. It is no longer an eagle, it is a chicken, even though it measures fifteen feet from tip to tip of its wings."

"No," said the naturalist, "it is an eagle still: it has the heart of an eagle, and I will make it soar high up to the heavens."

"No," said the owner, "it is a chicken, and it will never fly."

They agreed to test it. The naturalist picked up the eagle, held it up, and said with great intensity: "Eagle, thou art an *eagle*; thou dost belong to the sky and not to this earth; stretch forth thy wings and fly!"

The eagle turned this way and that, and then, looking

down, saw the chickens eating their food, and down he jumped.

The owner said: "I told you it was a chicken."

"No," said the naturalist, "it is an eagle. Give it another chance tomorrow."

So the next day he took it to the top of the house and said: "Eagle, thou art an eagle; stretch forth thy wings and fly." But again the eagle, seeing the chickens feeding, jumped down and fed with them.

Then the owner said: "I told you it was a chicken."

"No," asserted the naturalist, "it is an eagle, and it still has the heart of an eagle; only give it one more chance, and I will make it fly tomorrow."

The next morning he rose early and took the eagle outside the city, away from the houses, to the foot of a high mountain. The sun was just rising, gilding the top of the mountain with gold, and every crag was glistening in the joy of that beautiful morning.

He picked up the eagle and said to it: "Eagle, thou art an eagle; thou dost belong to the sky and not to this earth; stretch forth thy wings and fly!"

The eagle looked around and trembled as if new life were coming to it; but it did not fly. The naturalist then made it look straight at the sun. Suddenly it stretched out its wings and, with the screech of an eagle, it mounted higher and higher and never returned. It was an eagle, though it had been kept and tamed as a chicken!

When with great dramatic power Aggrey had told this story, he would say: "My people of Africa, we were created in the image of God, but men have made us think that we are chickens, and we still think we are; but we are eagles. Stretch forth your wings and fly! Don't be content with the food of chickens!"